YORK NOTES

My Oedipus Complex and Other Stories

Frank O'Connor

Note by Beverley Emm

 Longman York Press

Beverley Emm is hereby identified as author of this work in accordance with
Section 77 of the Copyright, Designs and Patents Act 1988

YORK PRESS
322 Old Brompton Road, London SW5 9JH

PEARSON EDUCATION LIMITED
Edinburgh Gate, Harlow,
Essex CM20 2JE, United Kingdom
Associated companies, branches and representatives throughout the world

First published 1999

ISBN 0–582–38194–0

Designed by Vicki Pacey
Phototypeset by Gem Graphics, Trenance, Mawgan Porth, Cornwall
Colour reproduction and film output by Spectrum Colour
Produced by Addison Wesley Longman China Limited, Hong Kong

CONTENTS

PREFACE

York Notes are designed to give you a broader perspective on works of literature studied at GCSE and equivalent levels. We have carried out extensive research into the needs of the modern literature student prior to publishing this new edition. Our research showed that no existing series fully met students' requirements. Rather than present a single authoritative approach, we have provided alternative viewpoints, empowering students to reach their own interpretations of the text. York Notes provide a close examination of the work and include biographical and historical background, summaries, glossaries, analyses of characters, themes, structure and language, cultural connections and literary terms.

If you look at the Contents page you will see the structure for the series. However, there's no need to read from the beginning to the end as you would with a novel, play, poem or short story. Use the Notes in the way that suits you. Our aim is to help you with your understanding of the work, not to dictate how you should learn.

York Notes are written by English teachers and examiners, with an expert knowledge of the subject. They show you how to succeed in coursework and examination assignments, guiding you through the text and offering practical advice. Questions and comments will extend, test and reinforce your knowledge. Attractive colour design and illustrations improve clarity and understanding, making these Notes easy to use and handy for quick reference.

York Notes are ideal for:
- Essay writing
- Exam preparation
- Class discussion

The author of these notes, Beverley Emm, is Head of English in a school in the East Riding, Yorkshire, and has considerable teaching experience at all high school age levels. She is an Assistant Principal Examiner for a major GCSE examination board.

The text used in these Notes is *My Oedipus Complex and Other Stories* by Frank O'Connor (Heinemann New Windmills, 1998).

Health Warning: This study guide will enhance your understanding, but should not replace the reading of the original text and/or study in class.

PART ONE

INTRODUCTION

HOW TO STUDY A SHORT STORY

You have bought this book because you wanted to study a collection of short stories, or an individual story, on your own. This may supplement work done in the class.

- You will need to read each story you are studying several times. Start by reading the story quickly for pleasure, then again slowly and carefully. Further readings will generate new ideas and help you to memorise the details of the story.
- Make careful notes on the themes, plots and characters you come across. Can you spot any themes which occur in more than one story?
- How is the story told? Is it narrated by one of the characters or by an all-seeing (omniscient) narrator who sees into the minds and motives of these imaginary beings?
- Which characters do you like or dislike? Why?
- A short story is different to a novel in lots of ways other than its length. Consider why the author might have chosen to use this method of writing, and how else it differs from other genres.
- Short stories need to have a strong beginning and end to contain the central idea or event. Which stories do this particularly well? Do you like or dislike any particular beginnings or endings?
- Some of the stories are very long, whilst some are very short indeed. Do you think that authors consider the length of their story to be important? What would be gained or lost from making them longer or shorter?

Studying on your own requires self-discipline and a carefully thought-out work plan in order to be effective. Good luck.

Frank O'Connor is the pseudonym of the writer Michael O'Donovan, born in Douglas Street, Cork in 1903.

Early life

Frank O'Connor, the only child of Michael and Mary O'Donovan, was born into a poor Irish family. He attended the Christian Brothers School in Cork but his parents could not afford to send him to university. This did not discourage the young writer, however, as he had always been interested in writing and reading, even from an early age. He was largely self-educated.

By the age of twelve, Frank O'Connor had already put together a collected edition of his work, consisting of poems, biographies and essays on Irish History. His early work was written in Gaelic, a language which he first learnt from listening to his grandmother before going on to study it formally. Frank O'Connor became fascinated with the history and legends of Ireland, immersing himself in Gaelic poetry, music and myth.

Instead of attending university, Frank O'Connor worked in a library, first in Cork and then in Dublin, a profession which allowed him the time to continue to educate himself and develop as a writer.

Later activities

Frank O'Connor became interested in Irish politics, and when the Civil War broke out in 1922, he joined the Irish Volunteers, fighting on the Republican side. He was held at a prisoner-of-war camp for a year, and after his release, began to publish his poems, stories and translations in the *Irish Statesman*. He was considered an important 'find' among young Irish authors.

In 1931, Frank O'Connor's first book, *Guests of the Nation*, was published, and the title story was reprinted in the *Atlantic Monthly*, the first of many Frank O'Connor stories which have since appeared in American magazines.

During his lifetime, Frank O'Connor lectured at Harvard University, Northwestern University and Trinity College, Dublin. For a time, he was also one of the directors of the famous Abbey Theatre in Dublin, an experience which he said gave him 'a lasting passion for techniques'. However, although he collaborated on a number of plays and published several books of verse, translations of Irish poetry, novels, criticisms, a biography and an autobiography, his particular art was that of the short story. He wrote hundreds, published in over thirty volumes, including *The Saint and Mary Kate* (1932), *The Wild Bird's Nest* (1932) and *Bones of Contention* (1936).

Frank O'Connor was a 'typical' Irishman. He had a charming accent, sharp wit and a contagious sparkle. He preferred to write in the mornings and sometimes in the evenings, leaving the afternoons free to cycle or walk about, looking in bookshops and talking to people he met. He was interested in architecture and had cycled through most of Ireland and large parts of England and France. His one complaint about America was that it didn't have cycle tracks. He was also somewhat of a student of eighteenth-century music.

Frank O'Connor was married twice, first to Evelyn Bowen, by whom he had two sons and a daughter, and later, in 1953, to Harriet Rich, an American girl from Annapolis, who gave him a second daughter. Frank O'Connor died in 1966.

His importance

W.B. Yeats once said that Frank O'Connor was 'doing for Ireland what Chekhov did for Russia'. Frank O'Connor's short stories, clearly rooted in Ireland and the Irish people, make a statement on the whole human condition. Frank O'Connor himself wrote: 'Story telling is the nearest thing one can get to the quality of a pure lyric poem. It doesn't deal with problems; it doesn't have any solutions to offer; it just states the human condition'. His stories exhibit a sense of reality, and demonstrate warmth and richness of character delineation, and often gentle humour. As V.S. Pritchett noted: 'It has often been said that Ireland is packed with genius but is short of talent. Frank O'Connor was one of a distinguished generation who had both ... One of the masters of the short story'.

CONTEXT & SETTING

The setting of the stories in this selection, both in terms of time and place, is very important. Frank O'Connor wrote about the life he knew, and his characters are formed and affected by his particular settings.

Time

All the stories are set in the first half of the twentieth century. It is possible to pinpoint the timing of some precisely, especially those concerning the character of Larry Delaney where a **chronological** (see Literary Terms) progression can be traced. The earliest of these, *My Oedipus Complex*, concentrates on the effects of Larry's father returning home after the First World War, so we can assume the events occur around 1918, when Larry is about five. This gives the story a certain social **context** (see Literary Terms), and focuses on an aspect of life that was crucial at the time, that of the difficulties of integrating war personnel into a civilian existence. By the time of *The Duke's Children*, however, Larry is a young man, and that story is therefore probably set in the nineteen thirties.

Place

With the exception of *The Paragon*, which takes place partly in England, all the short stories in this collection are set entirely in Ireland, and they all have a distinctly Irish 'flavour'. Events occur mostly in and around Cork

on the southern coast of Ireland, where Frank
O'Connor was born, but also at times in the city of
Dublin. There is a clear divide between city and country
life, and this forms the **theme** (see Literary Terms) of
several stories, for example, *Uprooted*. Specific names of
Irish places, such as Glengarriffe and Ballybeg, and
natural features, like the River Glen, are incorporated
into the stories, which adds a definite realism to the
events taking place. Irish names like Moll Mhor and
Thade Kendillon from *In The Train* also help to make
the stories authentic.

Social class

Many of the stories concern the poor people of Ireland,
either those living in rough areas such as Larry's family
in *The Genius*, who live in Barrackton, known locally as
the Barrack, or actual Irish peasants, living in remote
and isolated countryside, for example, Dan Bride in *The
Majesty of the Law* and Mrs Sullivan in *The Bridal
Night*. Irish culture is crucial to the stories of Frank
O'Connor, and the importance of the Irish working-
class community will be discussed more fully later (see
Theme on The Irish Community).

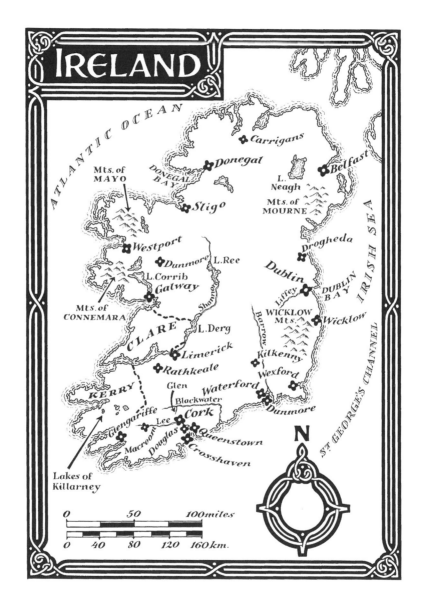

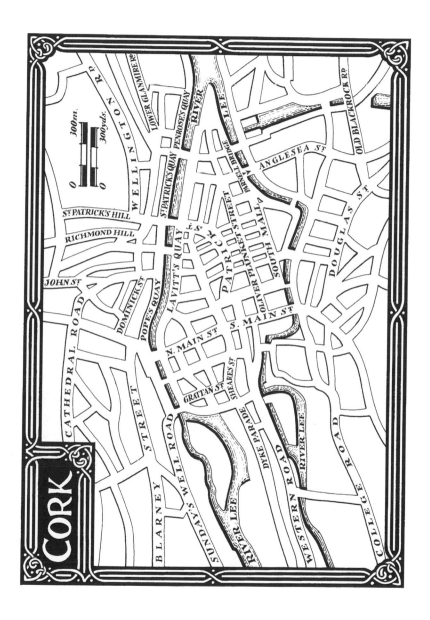

PART TWO

SUMMARIES

SECTION I: CHILDHOOD

MY OEDIPUS COMPLEX

The **narrator** (see Literary Terms) of this story is Larry Delaney, a character who appears in a number of Frank O'Connor's tales. In this one, he focuses on the life he creates for himself with his mother whilst his father is away at war, and how this paradise is shattered when his father returns.

Larry is very close to his mother. Every morning he climbs into her bed and discusses his plans for the day, which usually consist of going to church to pray for his father's safe return from the war. Larry lives an uncomplicated, idyllic existence: **ironically** (see Literary Terms), he describes the war as 'the most peaceful period of my life' (p. 13). His only complaint is the lack of a new baby in the house, which his mother teasingly tells him they cannot afford until his father returns because they cost seventeen and six.

His father's visits home do not disturb Larry, and he even takes pleasure in the fact that he comes and goes mysteriously like Santa Claus. At this stage, a man in the house is a novelty: Larry likes his father's smell, which is pleasant and musty from smoking, and he is impressed by seeing him shave.

Consider the situation from Larry's father's point of view – how easy is it for him?

However, this attitude soon changes when the war ends and Larry's father returns permanently. Suddenly, Larry has to compete for his mother's attention and he becomes very jealous. He resents being told to keep quiet because his mother is 'talking to Daddy', and also takes exception to constantly being told not to wake him. His mother tries to encourage a bond

between her husband and son but to no avail, and Larry
even contemplates praying to God to send his father
back.

Larry does everything in his power to annoy his father.
He feels indignant and incensed that this stranger has
intruded into his world and taken over his role as man
of the house. When his father threatens to smack his
bottom because he has been particularly naughty, Larry
can only scream in frustration and anger 'Smack your
own!' (p. 21).

Look at the ways
that his father
behaves childishly.

However, he is not alone in this resentment, and it
gradually becomes obvious that his father is also jealous.
They both act in very childish ways, conducting a series
of skirmishes against one another to win mother's
affection. Larry observes his father's behaviour and tries
to imitate him by inventing news to read to his mother
from the newspaper, making noises when drinking tea
and even dribbling into a pipe, all forms of behaviour
he thinks are attractive. All he succeeds in doing is
making a fool of himself and being called disgusting.

The situation is finally resolved when Larry's earlier
wish comes true, and a new baby is brought into the
family. Immediately mother becomes preoccupied,
focusing her attention on Sonny at the expense of both

Larry *and* his father. When Larry's father overhears
him talking to himself one day saying: 'If another
bloody baby comes into this house, I'm going out'
(p. 23), a link is established between them: for the first
time in the story they are on the same side. Larry now
considers his mother to be simple-minded and concedes
his father has a fine intelligence. When his father
comes in to Larry's room one night to escape his wife
trying to soothe a screaming baby, the bond between
them is finally sealed.

COMMENT   The term Oedipus Complex was coined by
psychoanalyst Sigmund Freud (1856–1939) to describe
a condition when a son has sexual feelings towards his
mother. It comes from a Greek myth concerning a man
called Oedipus who unknowingly kills his father, Laius,
and later marries his mother, Jocasta, again without
realising their true relationship. Here, Frank O'Connor
uses the term in a humorous way to convey how Larry
feels about his parents: he would dearly love to remove
his father from his life and, like many children, he talks
about marrying his mother when he is older so they can
have lots of babies. The reaction he receives – a smile
from his mother and a great guffaw from his father –
highlights how Frank O'Connor is gently mocking the
naive and innocent Larry.

One of the most significant things about this story is
the structure, and the changing **moods** (see Literary
Terms) and relationships throughout. At the beginning,
when Larry has his mother's undivided attention, a
peaceful **atmosphere** (see Literary Terms) is created
where he believes his life is simple, clear and full of
possibilities. However, the reality is that Larry is
thoroughly spoilt and is bound to find it very difficult
when a new authority figure is imposed upon him.

The middle part of the story focuses on the battle
between Larry and his father when they are outright

enemies. Both compete for the mother's attention, and because they are responding to events and feelings beyond their control, behave in very unreasonable and immature ways. The First World War may be over, but the use of war imagery, for example 'skirmishes', reminds us that fighting still continues on the domestic front.

Note the indications you find that the father is still being affected by his war experiences.

Although we view the story through Larry's eyes, it is useful here to consider it from other **viewpoints** (see Literary Terms). It is far from easy for his father to adapt to a more mundane way of life after being surrounded by the horrors of war, and his mother, too, is caught in the middle of her own conflict, this time between the two people in the world who mean the most to her. Both father and son behave as they do out of love for the mother, but the **irony** (see Literary Terms) is that she is the person being most adversely affected.

Find evidence where the mother is hurt by the actions of her husband and son.

By the end of the story, father and son have united in a common bond: they are both jealous of the new baby and the amount of time the mother devotes to him, and seek solace in each other's company. They also by now appreciate each other's feelings, and although neither of them apologises for their previously antagonistic behaviour, we are left with a feeling of optimism that from now on, their relationship will continue to develop in a positive way.

GLOSSARY

seventeen and six about 90p
petrified numb with cold
wax temper
vexed annoyed
indignity outrage, affront
cajoled coaxed
curios trinkets
obnoxious insufferable

flaking beating
magnanimous charitable, forgiving

THE GENIUS

This is another story with the young Larry as **narrator** (see Literary Terms), probably set in the immediate years after *My Oedipus Complex*. Having been told by his mother about geniuses, he decides he wants to become one. He is a bright child, interested in exploring, reading and writing books, and he vows to himself that he will one day be famous and have a statue put up in his honour.

Larry's parents treat him quite differently. Whilst his father would prefer a more 'manly' son, and envies his contemporaries who have 'normal, bloodthirsty, illiterate children' (p. 3), his mother is both protective and encouraging. When Larry is keen to know where babies come from, his father merely jokes that they are dropped from aeroplanes. However, his mother believes it is a matter of duty to explain properly, and does so using an **analogy** (see Literary Terms) a young child will understand. By the end of their conversation, Larry has established the fact that 'mummies had an engine in their tummies and daddies had a starting-handle that made it work' (p. 5). He accepts this at face value, his only reaction being to deplore the fact that he has no engine and buffers of his own, only a 'measly old starting-handle like Father' (p. 6).

In what other ways is Larry treated differently by his mother and father?

Larry finds it difficult making friends. He dislikes fighting and therefore prefers the company of girls. When he starts school, he has little in common with his own age group and is befriended by Una Dwyer, an older girl from the Senior school who has recently lost her younger brother, John Joe, in a car accident. Una's family comes from a more suburban area, and Larry

Consider how much this explains Una's interest in Larry.

feels comfortable in their presence, believing that they have a proper appreciation of geniuses.

One evening, when discussing John Joe's accident, Larry suggests to Una that she ask her mother to make her another brother, and reveals the secret of the engine and the starting-handle. By her reaction, he realises he has made a fool of himself but, never doubting the source of the story, assumes that his mother genuinely believes it. When Una comes to tea at the Delaneys' house, Larry is petrified that his mother will make a spectacle of herself by revealing her ignorance.

Notice how the humour is gradually built up during this scene.

The relationship between Larry and Una changes at the end of the story when Una finds herself a boyfriend of her own age. Larry describes this as the most tragic moment of his life. He feels totally inadequate: he is too young to marry Una, and does not even know where babies come from. He even regrets his previous attitude to fighting, and when he thinks of the other boy, wants only to batter his teeth and jump on his face. Despite being comforted by his mother, who recognises that he had reminded Una of her lost brother, Larry is inconsolable, and decides being a genius is a very lonely occupation.

COMMENT   This story is written in the **first person narrative** (see Literary Terms). It is told through the eyes of a young boy, but with an adult's perspective. Occasionally, comments made by the 'adult' Larry are included, for example: 'that is always the way it has happened to me. A woman has only to shut up and let me talk long enough for me to fall head and ears in love with her. But then I did not recognise the symptoms' (p. 7).

Because of this adult perspective, childlike ideas, such as wanting to know where babies come from and thinking he will grow up to marry his mother, are conveyed using a more mature and formal style. The effect of this is to show how seriously the young Larry takes himself, and convey to the reader how pompous and self-important he would appear to others. The reader is invited to mock Larry, but in a warm and gentle fashion. Much of the humour in the story is created by emphasising the difference between childhood and adulthood.

The title *The Genius* is **ironic** (see Literary Terms). Larry is certainly an interesting character, and conceivably demonstrates the potential to become a genius. He is inventive, shown at the start of the story by the way he avoids fighting, and also imaginative, creating his own Opera House where he not only builds the scenery and lighting but composes and sings all the songs. He is also confident and inquisitive. However, there is also an element of **paradox** (see Literary Terms) involved: whilst Larry may be a very articulate and intelligent young boy with aspirations to become the town's first proper genius, at heart he is still a very naive and innocent child, unsophisticated and gullible, with much to learn about the world.

As well as having the central **theme** (see Literary Terms) of childhood running throughout, the story also highlights other ideas such as first love, and the loneliness of being an outsider. The importance of Irish culture and its underlying religious influences are also touched upon.

GLOSSARY   **staff** a set of five horizontal lines on which music is written
solfa a system of syllables (doh, ray, me, fah, soh, la, te) used to represent the notes of the musical scale
Temperance drinking little or no alcohol
proscenium from the Greek proskenion, meaning stage
pertinacious persistent, determined

THE STUDY OF HISTORY

This is the story of how an intelligent child explores his origins and questions his parents' relationship. Larry has now grown to the age where he is beginning to see his mother and father as people in their own right rather than just as parents. He questions them about their past relationships, not only because he is inquisitive to learn more about them, but also because it allows him to imagine the person he might have been if either his mother or his father had married someone else.

Personal history becomes a fascination for Larry, and he soon learns that his parents both love to talk about it but in different ways. His mother discusses her history privately with Larry, recalling past feelings and events with nostalgia and sensitivity, whereas his father boasts openly about his previous conquests and seems to enjoy teasing his wife. The name which most arouses jealousy in Larry's mother is that of May Cadogan.

Why do you think his parents react in such different ways?

As part of his quest for self-discovery, Larry starts to frequent the road where Miss Cadogan, now Mrs O'Brien, lives. One evening, he asks a child playing nearby about her and is introduced first to Gussie, Mrs O'Brien's son, and then to May O'Brien herself, an attractive, laughing woman. She flirts with Larry and recalls the memory of his father, who she calls 'the old divil', in an exciting and intimate way.

Compare May Cadogan's behaviour with the way Larry's mother acts.

Initially fascinated, once inside her home Larry sees the life that might have been his: a large family with six children, uneducated and without manners; an untidy house with beds still unmade and scribbles on the walls; and a mother who, whilst kind and exhilarating, would never have nurtured a sensitive child like himself. Part of Larry regrets not belonging to such a fast-moving, colourful household but mostly he returns home that evening with a new appreciation of his own situation.

His parents react differently to the tale of his adventure: his father is pleased to be remembered by an old girlfriend as it feeds his ego, but his mother is very quiet and subdued, making Larry feel wretched and guilty. By the end of the day, Larry is quite unsettled by the range of emotions he has experienced. He knows that to have May Cadogan for a mother would require him to be a different type of person all together, and for a while he loses his sense of identity. Eventually, however, he is comforted by his mother, glad to feel safe and secure knowing he is once more where he belongs.

COMMENT   Larry's comment about Pascal not only shows his intelligence and wide ranging knowledge but also forms the premise on which this story is based. In his book 'Thoughts', Pascal wrote: 'If the nose of Cleopatra had been shorter, the whole face of the earth would have been changed'. This poses the question 'What if?' and relates directly to Larry's situation and growing inquisitiveness about life and about himself. To him, *The Study of History* opens up the possibilities of recreating it. He calls it 'the ultimate proof that things might have been different' (p. 25).

Frank O'Connor uses the **image** (see Literary Terms) of a sack to describe Larry grappling with adult concepts and finding them too difficult to handle at this stage in his life. Larry says: 'It was as though my own identity was a sort of sack I had to live in, and I had deliberately worked my way out of it, and now I couldn't get back again because I had grown too big for it' (p. 35). Larry is growing up, and as an intelligent child, starts to question his place in the world. However, what he finds unsettles him because it challenges the very foundations on which his life is built, and he is then made to feel even worse because he cannot retreat into the security of childhood without help.

This help comes in the form of his mother, a constantly reassuring presence in his young life. By holding her hand, the terror he feels at branching out into the adult world subsides. He says, again **metaphorically** (see Literary Terms): 'I became myself again, shrank into my little skin of identity, and left infinity and all its anguish behind' (p. 35). By expanding his knowledge and experience, Larry has reached out beyond the boundaries of his immediate world, and although he has temporarily retreated, he will continue this expansion throughout the rest of his life.

GLOSSARY   **ordained** destined, intended
Pascal Blaise Pascal, French mathematician (1623–1662)
countenance appearance, facial expression
enunciate pronounce
lambent soft, radiant with the sun

THE DUKE'S CHILDREN

This is the final story centred on Larry Delaney and here, Larry as a young man experiences some of the confusions of growing up as he starts work and widens his friendships.

Larry is convinced that he is a foundling, abandoned at birth by a wealthy royal family. He has nothing in

CHILDHOOD

How common are Larry's views on his parents to people of his age?

common with his parents and calls them common-place creatures. He is repelled by their poverty, their house, their friends and their conversations. The only explanation he can offer as to why his fate has become so strangely linked with such people is that he is really a duke, lost, stolen or strayed from his proper home.

One evening, Larry is befriended by Nancy Harding, a girl by whom he is soon bewildered and charmed. However, he feels very self-conscious of his humble background and when she wants to go home with him to borrow a book, is distraught at the prospect of her seeing his house and meeting his parents. Even though Nancy and his father chat away happily, Larry feels humiliated.

Larry contrasts his own father with Mr Harding, whom he respects. Whilst walking home with Nancy's father, he tries desperately to impress and finds himself making up lies about his accomplishments, especially his proficiency at foreign languages. He wants to be seen as good enough to be asked to the Hardings' home, but although he frequently walks past their house, he is never invited in. He believes it is because he is of a lower social class, and feels that when his true regal parentage is revealed, the Hardings will be the first to regret their blindness.

Compare May and Nancy to see why he feels more at ease in May's company.

Larry then meets up with a girl called May Dwyer, someone in whose presence he is immediately comfortable. He gets on well with her family, and feels completely at ease in her home.

What signs are there throughout the story that Nancy is actually ashamed of her father?

Some months later, he bumps into Nancy again, and it is clear from their conversation that she is jealous of his new relationship, especially because she believes May probably talks French and German fluently. Nancy becomes quite emotional and tells Larry the only reason he wasn't invited to her house was because she was ashamed of her sisters and her father.

Lack of experience in relationships stops Larry sorting out the confusion, and it is only years later that he realises he and Nancy had so much in common, both of them an outcast in their respective families, both so desperate to impress that they were living above and beyond themselves. With the wisdom of maturity and hindsight, Larry comes to understand that she, too, was one of the Duke's children.

COMMENT

This is a sad story, and there is a feeling of discontentment throughout. Frank O'Connor uses the **first person narrative** (see Literary Terms) so that we can experience Larry's dissatisfaction with his life and his parents in particular, and understand why he feels so unhappy. He also uses the clever technique of Larry's internal voice, which conveys his fantasy world and highlights the difference between the person he is and the person he would like to be.

Find examples of this internal voice– at what point is the fantasy world shattered?

At times, it is hard to sympathise with Larry. It is not until we realise that he is acting through inexperience and with all the conflicting emotions of youth that we can fully appreciate his actions. By the end of the story, the adult Larry has managed to analyse his earlier feelings, especially his attraction to Nancy, who he calls his first and purest love. The **mood** (see Literary Terms) is quite wistful as he contemplates what might have been.

This story highlights the **themes** (see Literary Terms) of first love, and the loneliness of being an outsider. Again, the importance of Irish culture and its underlying religious influences are also touched upon.

GLOSSARY

fatuous foolish
patrimony family
ducal duke-like

A *Identify the speaker.*

1 This time, for all her quiet air, I knew that she meant it, and knew that my principal rights and privileges were as good as lost unless I asserted them at once

4 I saw that love was a game that two people couldn't play at without pushing, just like football

2 In the end, of course, I did nothing at all; I had no experience to indicate to me what I could do

3 Being good at reading would never satisfy her

Identify the person 'to whom' this comment refers.

5 'She was a bit old for you. You reminded her of her little brother that was killed, of course – that was why'

6 He was very bony but better than nothing

8 I hoped she felt as she looked. It seemed to me that she deserved it all

7 'The man is an out-and-failure, and he's managed to turn Mother into one as well'

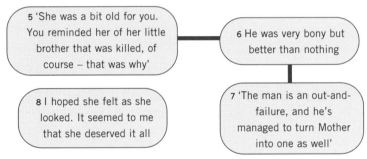

Check your answers on page 84.

  B *Consider these issues.*

a How we are able to see the development of Larry Delaney through all four stories.

b How the character of the young Larry is conveyed through a combination of humour and seriousness.

c The difference between Larry's father and mother, and the effect this has on Larry.

d The way other people treat Larry and how he would like to be treated.

e How important it is that these stories are set in an Irish community.

The bridal night

The Bridal Night is set in a remote and lonely part of Ireland. It concerns Denis Sullivan, a young man who has gradually declined into madness. Denis currently lives in an asylum in Cork, and his mother, in conversation with a stranger, recalls the events leading up to his committal.

What effect is created by having one of the characters involved tell the story?

The problems began when a teacher, Miss Regan, moved into the area. Being a stranger and not being Irish, she was ignored by most of the small community. Miss Regan enjoyed sitting in the wild countryside by the sea, reading, and this was when Denis first spotted her. They became friends, and she used to joke that Denis was her beau and her intended, although his mother recalls she meant no harm by it.

When Miss Regan realised Denis was beginning to want more than friendship, she tried to avoid him, and it was this that triggered his madness. His mother took pains to discourage him, knowing that Miss Regan was not the sort to marry, but Denis could hardly sleep or eat and in his troubled state of mind, took to wandering at night.

One day, Denis woke 'roaring', and because he was very strong, his mother could not control him. She sought

help from the Donoghues, her good neighbours, who
eventually managed to rope Denis into his bed until he
was quiet and the doctor could attend him. They
arranged for him to be committed the next day, and
Sean Donoghue agreed to remain there for the night
because it was not safe for Mrs Sullivan to be alone
with her son.

Denis, in his delirious state, began to call for 'Winnie',
and his mother thought he might calm down if he
could just see Miss Regan for a while. She was very
thankful that the school teacher agreed to come, but
became embarrassed when Denis suggested Miss Regan
get into bed with him, claiming it was just the madness

Think about why
Frank O'Connor
chose to call this
story The Bridal
Night.

talking. However, Miss Regan knew this was the only
thing that would calm Denis, and disregarding both her
safety and her reputation, she slept the night there.
When his mother looked in on them, she saw Denis
sleeping like a child without a care in the world.

The following morning, Denis's mother knelt before
Miss Regan and kissed her hands, such was her
gratitude. The teacher left for school, promising Denis
she would return, and when the police came to take
Denis away, he went quietly.

The story ends with Mrs Sullivan recalling the reaction
of the community. Not only did people fail to judge
Miss Regan harshly, they recognised the kindness of
her actions and couldn't do enough for her. In a world
where people are always ready to assume the worst,
Denis's mother finds the response of the
neighbourhood both strange and wonderful.

COMMENT   This is an unusual and interesting short story, almost
moving in its simplicity. It starts with a vivid
description (see Literary Terms) of the rural Irish
landscape, thereby emphasising the importance of the
remote and wild setting to the events about to unfold.

Frank O'Connor places Denis's mother into this scene, sitting on the low stone wall outside her cottage, and immediately we can **empathise** (see Literary Terms) with the extreme isolation and loneliness of this old woman.

The weather is used throughout the story to reflect mood, a technique known as **pathetic fallacy** (see Literary Terms). At times, the turbulence of the weather is clearly mirrored in the growing agitation of Denis. When the wind blows up from the sea, he begins to rave, and Sean Donoghue knows Denis will get worse as the night goes on and the wind rises. The use of this technique adds to the disturbed **atmosphere** (see Literary Terms) of the story.

A distinct sense of community is evoked in *The Bridal Night*, for example, the Donoghues willingly help their elderly neighbour in her time of need. As with many close-knit neighbourhoods, however, they do not take kindly to strangers moving into the area, and Miss Regan is mostly ignored, especially as the only Irish thing about her is the book she reads.

What evidence can you find to show that Mrs Sullivan in particular is religious? Consider the risks Miss Regan was taking by behaving in this way.

This attitude might give her particular cause to refuse to help Denis, and the fact that the people are so obviously religious means they are even more likely to frown upon her actions. However, Miss Regan is prepared to ignore the possible repercussions to herself and sacrifice her reputation in order to help Denis.

When the local people discover what she has done, they recognise that her actions were undertaken through kindness, and no-one speaks a bad word about what she did. From that day on until the time she moves away from the area, she is accepted as part of the community.

GLOSSARY

belie misrepresent
'baccy tobacco
stirabout porridge

praties potatoes
cnuceen small hill
forninst behind
asthore an expression of affection, for example, treasure

IN THE TRAIN

We are first introduced to the sergeant and his wife sitting on a train waiting for it to leave the station. Having been in the city for a few days, they are returning to the country, but the sergeant's wife is very disparaging about her home town because she feels it has no life: she dislikes the place, the people and the weather.

They notice other people arriving on the train, including Magner and some other policemen, and a group of peasants, her 'charming' neighbours, who are wild and laughing and shouting defiantly. To both groups she is outwardly polite but secretly scornful.

Just as the train is about to start, a mysterious-looking young woman, who we later learn is Helena Maguire, tries to join their compartment, but all three people, who obviously recognise each other, react adversely, and the young woman runs away to find another carriage. The train subsequently sets off on its journey.

Notice the descriptions of city life compared with the country. The focus then shifts to the four policemen. They discuss how much they dislike the sergeant's wife, and the merits of living in the city rather than the country. We learn that they have been state witnesses in a legal case, and that whilst in court, they were unnerved by seeing the poison mug and a model of the house back in Farranchreesht where the incident occurred.

Think about the reasons why these people would lie for Helena. The final shift is to the country folk, where Moll Mhor and Thade Kendillon are bickering. They are discussing Helena, the accused, who is a woman from their village,

and acknowledge the lies each of them has told on her
behalf in court, even though they all believe she is guilty
of the crime. When the policemen join them, they, too,
are aware that Moll is 'the biggest and brazennest and
cleverest liar of the lot' (p. 125).

Meanwhile, Helena Maguire is reliving her experiences
in court, and her fear up to the point she was found not
guilty. Magner arrives to congratulate her on the result,
whilst at the same time, still pushing her to confess.
Helena says the acquittal was the holy will of God, but
Magner insists it was all down to Moll's lies.

Do you feel any sympathy with Helena for her ordeal?

Magner makes a rather cryptic comment about Helena
now having the man she wanted, and the story ends
with the train arriving at its destination and Helena
looking pensively out of the window at the approaching
water's edge.

COMMENT

This is a complex story, cleverly crafted and with a very
distinctive structure. It is divided into different sections,
each of the earlier ones introducing a series of new
characters to the reader without immediately making it
clear who they are or why they are there. The main plot
is pieced together by a number of clues throughout the
story, and it is only at the very end that all the pieces of
the jigsaw finally fall into place.

Find the clues we are given throughout the story.

Because all the action takes place on board a train, the
setting is confined, and therefore these characters are
unable to avoid interaction. We gradually learn that
they are figures in the trial of Helena Maguire, a
woman accused of murdering a man by poison. The
fact that the characters include witnesses for the
prosecution and the defence, and also the accused
woman herself, makes for inevitable conflict.

The **theme** (see Literary Terms) of the Irish
community is prominent. The country folk seem
initially to have little sympathy with Helena Maguire

and resent her impudence at returning to live in
Farranchreesht because it is such a decent place.
However, they are quite prepared to lie for her because
she is a woman in their parish: she is *one* of the
community. When accused of swearing black was
white, Thade Kendillon replies: 'What else would
I do, woman? There was never an informer in my
family' (p. 124). Even the police are good-natured in
their accusations and Magner speaks with a tone of
admiration and genuine respect when he calls her a
clever and remarkable woman. Belief in community
seems to outweigh belief in justice.

The story ends on an **ambiguous** (see Literary Terms)
note. A drunken Magner comments on the one man in
the village who will be happy because it is 'his turn
now'. He says: 'Your people wouldn't let you have him
but you have him now in spite of them all' (p. 129).
This could suggest that the man in question, Cady
Driscoll, is Helena's lover, and that she murdered her
husband so that they could be together. However, she
denies that he means anything to her. We are left with
the feeling that although the jigsaw, in many respects,
is complete, maybe several of the pieces are, in reality,
still missing.

GLOSSARY   **equability** steadiness
                simulacrum an unreal image, a phantom
                jorum a colloquial term for a glass of alcohol
                squiffy slightly drunk
                stupefaction a stunned state
                mawkish sentimental
                dissipated wasted, thin

THE MISER

The miser of the title is Tom Devereux, a repulsive
man with bleary, bloodshot eyes who runs a dirty little

shop. He is a solitary character, tormented by the local children and looked after reluctantly by Faxy, his ex-army servant. Devereux is the last in line of a wealthy family, and most of the townspeople assume he is a miser, secretly hoarding a fortune whilst living in squalor.

Look closely at the relationship between Devereux and Faxy.

When Devereux has a stroke and is unable to work, Faxy runs the shop for him, but they argue constantly and the old man is convinced he is being cheated. Thinking Devereux is about to die, a local man of the church, Father Ring, becomes involved, outwardly concerned about Devereux's well-being but inwardly far more interested in whether he has made a will. He arranges for two nuns to come in to look after Devereux, even though the old man insists he cannot afford it.

Think about why Devereux becomes so accepting of the nuns yet Faxy doesn't.

The nuns make a tremendous difference to the household and to Devereux himself, making them both clean and presentable again. Devereux is at first resentful and then appreciative, but Faxy remains hostile.

One day, Father Ring suggests Devereux get his affairs in order and offers to write his will. After being subtly manipulated, Devereux agrees to leave money to the church. He is still convinced Faxy has robbed him, but when Faxy bursts in the room to argue, obviously having been listening at the door, he reluctantly agrees to leave him something, although only in the hope that it will 'choke' him. The will becomes the talk of the town, with everyone having an opinion as to who is the greediest, and who the most deserving to inherit the fortune.

Devereux takes a great liking to one of the nuns and begins to make an improvement under her care. When he does eventually die, she seems genuinely upset. Father Ring and Faxy, however, are more concerned with opening the great iron-bound chests to get their hands on Devereux's fortune.

It comes as a great shock to everyone to discover that the chests are full of nothing but screws, bolts, and bits of broken vases. After getting builders in to rip apart the house, the two men are forced to accept the fact that Devereux had, indeed, been as poor as he claimed. They are very disappointed, but Father Ring is forced to concede that Devereux was a remarkable man.

COMMENT

This story presents a view of the Irish community that is not particularly favourable, and the characters are all portrayed negatively. However, there are possibly redeeming features about each of them, and we are left to judge for ourselves as to who, if any, deserve our sympathies.

Can you find any other positive comments made about Devereux?

Frank O'Connor's powerful description of both Tom Devereux and his environment is particularly repugnant, and serves to eliminate any compassion the reader might feel for what is, essentially, a pitiful old man. However, we are told that he originally came from a respectable family, but made the mistake of marrying beneath him, and his daughter, too, turned out badly. Maybe we are meant to infer that fate, rather than Devereux himself, is to blame for his current predicament.

The fact that Faxy chooses to endure disgusting conditions and treatment for the sake of stealing cigarettes, along with the prospect of future gain, makes him, too, an unpleasant character. However, he does look after Devereux, not a particularly thankful task, and he is owed money in back wages. Even Father Ring admits he is entitled to something.

Consider the overall impression given of religion in this story.

Father Ring is just as bad, if not worse: as a man of the church, surely he should be above such mercenary behaviour. He is scheming and manipulative, but does not act directly for personal gain, aiming to acquire wealth for the church.

At first the nuns appear unsympathetic and almost ruthless, although the fact that 'the sergeant-major' grows to like Devereux and spends her time reading to him and holding his hand probably redeems her. Even then, however, there is a suggestion that because he praises her and makes her feel good, she may be thinking more of her own feelings than his.

The townsfolk gossip about Tom Devereux and his supposed fortune. It is presumably a small community, where everyone knows everyone else's business, and the Devereux family had become something of a legend. The people have an opinion on everyone concerned: Devereux is considered hard and unnatural and Father Ring is grasping. Their one saving grace, though, is their attitude at the end when Father Ring, desperately looking for the missing fortune, has a nasty feeling that the crowd will be well-pleased if he fails.

Nothing is presented to us as conclusive in this story: we are very much left to make up our own minds as to who is right and who is wrong. What Frank O'Connor does do, however, especially by constructing such a twist at the end, is to make a comment on the nature of greed and thwarted expectations, and leave the issue with us.

GLOSSARY   **masher** an affected fashionable womaniser
               batman an army officer's servant
               baksheesh payment
               sahib Indian word meaning lord and master
               tiffin Indian word for meal
               perspicacity clear understanding

THE MAJESTY OF THE LAW

Old Dan Bride lives a rustic existence in a little cottage with only his dog for company. When the local policeman arrives one evening, he welcomes him and they exchange pleasantries, both treating each other with respect.

Encouraged to stay for a while, the sergeant accepts a drink of what he knows is illegal whisky, and they discuss the lost art of distilling. Dan also has tea and home-made bread for his guest, a 'sure sign that he had

Consider why both been expecting a visitor' (p. 145). They both relax in
men behave in this front of the log fire, and are content and comfortable in
way. each other's company.

When twilight descends, the policeman pleasantly leaves, but returns minutes later and asks Dan, very politely, if he intends to pay the fine he owes. Dan, with just as much respect, says he does not, which is the answer the sergeant is expecting. They both acknowledge this matter is the real reason for the visit. The sergeant suggests that many in the community would willingly pay the fine for Dan if he cannot afford it, but Dan's reason is not based on finances, it is because he refuses to give 'that fellow' the satisfaction of paying.

When the sergeant mentions he has a warrant for Dan's arrest, Dan offers to go with him there and then, but he is told to make the trip to prison at his own convenience and they agree on Friday.

Only at the very end of the story do we discover Dan's crime: he 'had the grave misfortune to open the head of another old man in such a way as to require his removal to hospital' (p. 149). He thinks by going to prison rather than paying the fine, he will be punishing the other man: it is a matter of principle.

On the agreed day, Dan walks to the prison, accompanied by many of his friends who have come to wish him well, and sees the old man, the victim, hastily making his way indoors to avoid the neighbours.

COMMENT

Look closely at the descriptive passages to see how Frank O'Connor creates this mood of contentment.

The Majesty of the Law presents an unusual picture of legal justice. Both men know that Dan has committed a crime, that he has been punished by receiving a fine, and that he has no intention of paying it. The policeman arrives with the warrant for Dan's arrest, and Dan is expecting him. Yet they go through what could be seen as a charade, chatting politely like old friends. Such a warm and peaceful **atmosphere** (see Literary Terms) is created that we are lulled into a false sense of security: it comes as something of a shock to discover the real reason for the visit.

Appreciating the importance and strength of the community is essential to understanding the behaviour of both men. We are shown how close knit the neighbourhood is: the people are willing to pay Dan's fine, they all come to shake him by the hand before he sets off for prison, and the old man who is the victim is too ashamed to face them because he has set the law on 'one of his own'.

There is an automatic bond between Dan and the sergeant because they are both members of this community. The policeman does not want to be there, shown by his desire to disassociate himself from his duties, and once they have agreed on Friday, he speaks with relief that the delicate matter is now settled. Equally, Dan does not wish to cause any inconvenience to the sergeant, and shows through his manner that he apportions no blame on the man who is presenting him with such an 'unneighbourly document'.

Dan is the person who has hospitalised a man, yet our sympathies lie with him, not least because of how everyone else reacts towards him. He is prepared to suffer for his principles, knowing that his actions will bring shame to the victim and his family. He understands that he will have the respect and admiration of the community, and this is worth suffering a few nights in prison.

GLOSSARY   **brosna** decayed twigs, kindling
             imperturbability calmness, coolness

Identify the speaker.

1 'We'll get you the next time, though'

2 'oh, by the way, I nearly forgot it; my head is going – I suppose your own little affairs are in order?'

4 'I'll tell him you're coming, and I'll guarantee when he knows you're a friend of mine he'll make you as comfortable as if you were at home'

3 'I'll stop here with him and he'll go fast asleep'

Identify the person 'to whom' this comment refers.

5 The madness was on him, even then, and it was only when I saw the plunder done that I knew there was no cure for him only to put her out of his mind entirely

6 she was an incurable scandal-monger and mischiefmaker who couldn't keep quiet about her own business, much less about that of her neighbours

8 the dirt and disorder round him grew and greased his hair and clothes, while his face and chin with their Buddha-like gravity were shiny with spilt gravy

7 He sat in his old place by the fire, took out his pipe once more, blew through it thoughtfully, and just as he leaned forward for a twig to kindle it, heard the steps returning

Check your answers on page 84.

Consider these issues.

a The effect of belonging to a close-knit Irish community.

b How the Irish countryside is portrayed as wild and lonely.

c The sharp difference between city and country life.

d The importance and influence of religion in these stories.

e How some country people have an unusual attitude to law-breaking.

Section III: Love

The ugly duckling

Nan Ryan is the sister of Mick Courtney's best friend, Dinny. As a child she is ugly, with a stocky, sturdy figure and masculine features. A fierce, tough tomboy, she is the youngest of four children and the only girl.

By her early teenage years, Nan has grown out of this stage and has become quite religious, declaring she wants to be a nun. She starts to wear more feminine clothes, and it amuses Mick to discover she has a crush on him. Nan is a complex character: she finds it difficult to make friends, acts and talks like an older woman with none of the vibrancy and spontaneity associated with youth, and despite being intelligent, foregoes a college education to work in a dress shop.

Look in detail at this 'transformation scene'.

One night, Nan misunderstands a friendly gesture from Mick and kisses him. It is only at this point that Mick realises how Nan has grown into a girl of striking beauty, and although he doesn't respond immediately, he gradually drops his steady girlfriend and begins to visit the Ryan household more and more.

Nan has plenty of admirers, especially Joe Lyons, a solicitor, and Matt Healy, a butter merchant, but she has no objection to being courted by Mick as she still has a childish infatuation with him. However, when Mick eventually proposes, she makes a joke of it and tells him he doesn't have enough money.

Consider why this trip changes Nan so much.

Nan and a girlfriend spend a few days away with Lyons and Healy, and this trip seems to change Nan: she becomes very brooding and intense. She agrees to Mick's proposal, on the condition that he becomes more ambitious and they move to Dublin. With definite plans for the future, Mick becomes very focused, and he grows more attractive and reckless, qualities which make Nan both admire and love him.

Think about the sort of life they would have had if Nan had accepted Mick's proposal.

However, Nan continues to see her other suitors, and although Mick is not really jealous, they have a row one evening and Nan says she cannot marry him after all. Although Mick apologises, he realises that their quarrel is not the real cause of Nan's unhappiness. He then receives a note from her saying she intends to marry Joe Lyons.

Mick moves to Dublin as arranged and within a year, has met and married a girl called Eilish. When he accidentally bumps into Dinny, he discovers that Nan has joined a convent, having dropped Lyons after a couple of months. This confuses Mick: he still has no idea what had made her so unhappy and comes to the conclusion that all her decisions were made because of some inner torment.

The story ends when Mick returns to Cork many years later after the death of his father, and visits Nan at the convent. Nan is delighted to see him, and he tries hard to fathom the reasons behind her being so unsettled in the past and so happy and enthusiastic about life now. When he leaves, he has come to a better understanding. He also recognises that although they are both content in their chosen lives, they obviously still feel a great deal for one other, and always will.

COMMENT

The Ugly Duckling is not a love story in the conventional sense, but it does deal with the close relationship between Nan and Mick and shows how their feelings endure despite the passage of time.

Look at Mrs Ryan's words and consider their effect on Nan.

The story is separated into three parts, with Nan Ryan growing from childhood to adulthood as the sections progress, and although she obviously changes as she develops, Nan's complexity and feelings of being different remain constant throughout.

In the first section, Nan seems to turn to religion as a refuge from her nightmares, and also to escape from her mother's unkind taunts about her appearance. By the second section, religion is forgotten as Nan relishes the novelty of growing from *The Ugly Duckling* into a beautiful swan, as in Hans Christian Anderson's fairytale, and she experiments with adult relationships, including, we assume, a sexual 'indiscretion' with Joe Lyons.

However, in this middle section, Mick comes to realise that Nan is desperate about herself. She is very unsettled, shown by her desire to move to Dublin with Mick, and when she tells him, 'I don't mind if you make a mess of it. It's not failure I'm afraid of. It's just getting stuck in the mud, not caring for anything' (p. 76), she could just as easily be talking about herself. Even being engaged does not bring Nan peace of mind: she is scared of marriage itself and knows, deep down, that Mick is wrong for her. Breaking off the engagement is almost an act of self-sacrifice, and even Dinny tells Mick that by pursuing Nan further, he will only be hurt even more.

It comes as little surprise, then, to learn in the final section that Nan has fulfilled her earlier declaration and become a nun. The unhappiness which fuelled her perpetual restlessness has vanished, and instead, speaking with a delighted laugh, she acknowledges that God came first.

Mick can at last recognise the reasons behind the route Nan has chosen. He sees that people like her, who feel inadequate as children, create an interior world into which they can escape. When their inadequacies disappear, the freedom of the real world proves too difficult for them to cope with, and they are unhappy, even with those they love best. The only solution is to retreat into their interior world, which is what Nan has done, and she at last seems comfortable with herself. It is a testament to their deep feelings that the love and affection they share continues, even though they are both now content with their chosen lives.

GLOSSARY

Amazon female warrior

novenas devotion consisting of special prayers or services on nine successive days

gait manner of walking

sans-culottes a term from the French Revolution of 1789, literally translated as 'without trousers' but here used to mean a revolutionary

agnostic non-believer

dividends profits

beaux boyfriends

complaisance quiet satisfaction

braggadocio empty boasting

parochial provincial, unrefined

DON JUAN'S TEMPTATION

In literature, a Don Juan is traditionally seen as a character famed for his attractive qualities who enjoys seducing women. In this story, the Don Juan in question is Gussie Leonard, who is envied by men for his captivating charms with the opposite sex.

Consider which type of girl a real Don Juan would find attractive.

Gussie meets Helen at a party and is attracted by her naturalness. He walks her home and en route, asks her to spend the night with him. When she refuses, he tries to pass off his proposition as a harmless little joke, and is annoyed that some busybodies at the party had warned her off.

The two converse on the journey back to Helen's flat. When she asks about Gussie's other girlfriends, he boasts of several, both married and single, and they argue about his attitude to women and whether he truly likes them. Helen is more than a match for him, and this attracts Gussie to her even more. At times their

LOVE

sparring takes the form of light-hearted teasing and flirting, but in addition, they aim insults at each other that show anger and are hurtful. Helen's tone is one of 'mingled fascination and loathing' (p. 90).

Gussie is rather patronising, assuming he is far more experienced than Helen, and in a cynical way, accuses her of sentimental romanticism. However, how Gussie appears on the outside is not how he really is. When he thinks with self-pity back to his lonely youth, conceding that he was unsure of himself and just as idealistic as Helen, we learn of a different side to him.

How alike do you think Helen and Joan really are?

Before leaving Helen at her flat, Gussie asks to see her again because he still has hopes of 'converting' her into someone who will sleep with him. He then takes a walk by the canal, and realises the attraction of Helen is that she reminds him of Joan, a girl he knew in his youth. He and Joan had experienced a deep affection, something complete and perfect, even though their relationship was non-sexual and short: Joan already had a disease which was to kill her in six months. He sees that Helen is similar to Joan, and is tempted to embark upon a genuine committed relationship with her.

Consider why Gussie greets Helen 'almost petulantly'.

However, when he returns home, Helen is waiting for him, ready to accede to his wishes and spend the night. Gussie is initially annoyed that she has been converted after all, but soon reverts to his confident, womanising self, grateful that he has not succumbed to the temptation of a lifetime.

COMMENT

Don Juan's Temptation shows the sexual nature of male/female relationships, but the fact that Gussie Leonard is not a typical Don Juan means that the story is not just about sex but also about love. Gussie behaves as he does because events in his past have made a lasting impression on him. In a way, he is protecting himself from being hurt again by building protective barriers around his emotions, sleeping with as many women as possible to avoid becoming close to one, thereby making himself vulnerable. He maintains a sophisticated, assured image but it is all just an outward show. It is this hidden side to Gussie that makes him a redeeming character.

Gussie's reaction to finding Helen waiting for him is a sad note on which to end the story. If she had not been quite so easily 'converted', it is possible that he would have given in to temptation. After all, whilst reminiscing about Joan, he does admit he would give anything to be able to feel like that about a woman again, and although he feels frightened and weak at the thought, he seems ready to take the risk.

However, after an initial reaction of irritation, he gradually comes to feel relief at Helen's presence. He believes he has been through a terrible temptation and is overjoyed to have resisted. Because Helen is there, Gussie can quickly reestablish the facade he presents to the world. He can play it safe and not take any risk, an infinitely safer option but with far less potential of lasting happiness.

GLOSSARY

camaraderie friendship
umbrage offence, resentment
blackguard scoundrel
orthodoxy conservatism, convention
sanatorium a clinic or hospital, often with patients suffering from tuberculosis
petulantly irritably
decorous polite, straitlaced

A salesman's romance

This story shows the fickle nature of romance, and depicts how quickly attraction can change to dislike. It concerns Charlie Ford, a confident, outgoing man, who is such a proficient commercial traveller that he is considered an artist in his own right, and Celia Halligan, his fiancée.

One evening, driving home from the Red Cow, they have an accident with a jaunting car which is

Consider how far Charlie's attitude to driving explains his keenness to prove his innocence.

unlit and on the wrong side of the road. Charlie, who is an excellent driver and boasts that he has been driving for fifteen years without an accident, manages to avoid a catastrophe and no-one is hurt. The jarvey, however, who is very drunk, sees it as an opportunity to make a profit, and the case ends up going to court.

On the day of the trial, the jarvey, represented by Michael Dunn, an old acquaintance of Celia's, is plausible but boring, and when Charlie takes the stand, he realises that his salesmanship techniques should win

In what way are Charlie's salesmanship techniques exhibited in court?

the day. He puts on the performance of a lifetime, entertaining the court and completely winning over the judge. He makes a fool of Dunn who gets him to admit he had consumed three drinks, only later to be told they were lemonades. When Charlie states his opinion that only a dangerous lunatic would drink and drive, the judge is even more impressed.

All is well until Celia takes the stand. Immediately, Dunn makes the court feel prejudiced against her because she had been drinking whisky, and the judge takes an instant dislike to her. For every question asked, Charlie gives a brilliant answer in his head but unfortunately hears the real one. He recognises that Celia has no salesmanship, and even though he wins the case, it brings him little satisfaction.

Charlie is later surprised and irritated to discover that on the evening of the case, Celia had gone to a dance with Michael Dunn, stating he had only been doing his job as a lawyer when he had cross-examined her. Charlie is even more upset when Celia returns his ring and tells him she intends to marry Dunn. He finds this completely unreasonable and takes to drink for months. However, he soon realises how the fact that he 'won the case and lost the girl' makes a good story to use with prospective customers. With this, he has turned the situation to his advantage and become himself once more.

COMMENT   This story shows how one incident can completely change people's feelings for one another, but it also questions how genuine those feelings are in the first place.

Celia is described as a handsome woman, with 'a dirty tongue and an attitude of cynical but good-humoured contempt for men' (p. 104). Because Charlie is such an extrovert, interested in salesmanship for its own sake, he behaves like he is selling something even when he is not, and it is his ability to make Celia look and feel good that makes him so attractive to her. Even though she is normally sceptical, she 'could not resist the coloured enlargement of herself that Charlie presented to her in a gilt frame' (p. 104). Maybe it is because the relationship is built on such shaky and shallow foundations that it is so easily destroyed at the end.

The court case provides the focus for both Charlie and
Celia to reconsider their feelings. Charlie expects Celia
to be like him and is distraught when she begins to
answer Dunn's questions because she has learned
nothing from his example. He goes through agonies
listening to her giving evidence, and it is with despair
that he realises she lacks salesmanship. Similarly, when
she has finished giving evidence, Celia is sulky and
furious, and rejects Charlie's falsely comforting hand as
though he is to blame for everything. Ultimately, both
Charlie and Celia value superficial appearances above
their romance, and it is little wonder their relationship
soon fails.

GLOSSARY   **jaunting car** an Irish horse-drawn carriage
              jarvey carriage driver
              ascetic-looking severe, strict
              impudent arrogant, disrespectful
              courtesan prostitute

UPROOTED

*Notice the
differences
between the two
brothers in the
opening pages of
the story.*

Uprooted tells the tale of two brothers, Ned and Tom
Keating, who originate from the country but who are
currently living in the city of Dublin. Ned, on the one
hand, is a school teacher, and although previously had
been fiercely determined to move away from home, he
now finds the mundane and isolated city life hard to
bare. His only friend is a nurse, but shyness and caution
keep him from making any commitment. Tom, on the
other hand, is very different from his brother: a curate,
he is friendly, humorous, outgoing and at ease in
everybody's company.

One Easter, Tom suggests they both travel home for
the weekend to visit their family. Their household is
traditionally Irish: a cottage in the hillside with
whitewashed walls and oil lamps, which never seems

to change. Even the conversation his parents are
having when they arrive seems to Ned to be the same
as on his last visit. Tom, in particular, feels at home
again immediately, and joins in with the local gossip
that his father, Tomas, enjoys recalling so dramatically.

Tomas arranges a visit for Ned and Tom to meet up
with their mother's family, the O'Donnells, who live on
an island across the bay. He claims the purpose is for
them to see their cousins, but no-one is under any
allusions as to the real reason: he wants to be able to
drink plenty of alcohol without encountering the wrath
of his wife. During the boat journey, Tomas admits
this, but also explains he organised the outing because
he is a proud father, wanting to show off Tom and Ned.

They meet up with many of their relatives and Tomas
soon disappears to get drunk. During dinner, Tom asks
after the Deignan family, especially the three daughters,
as he jokingly says he wants a decent girl for his
brother. Everyone loudly suggests Cait.

When they visit the Deignan sisters, Ned is struck by
Cait's beauty. Tom is his usual friendly self and flirts
with the girls, but when he tells Cait that Ned is
looking for a wife, and everyone else laughs, Ned feels
uncomfortable.

They all set off to meet up with Tomas but a storm descends, and Cait offers to share her shawl with Ned in an attempt to keep them dry. Ned is so affected by this experience he feels he has 'dropped out of Time's pocket' (p. 192). They wait in the kitchen and Ned continues to be aware of Cait, especially when he catches her secretly looking at him. He is at once filled with passion and loneliness. A very drunken Tomas finally arrives and the men set off in the boat for home. As Ned waves goodbye to Cait, he experiences a feeling of both exultation and loss.

The following day, both brothers have to return to the city once more. Tom wakes after a bad night's sleep, and confesses to Ned that he, too, is troubled. Although he appears outwardly content, he feels just as lonely as Ned, and his occupation in the church only increases his isolation. Whereas before Ned had been jealous, he now realises that Tom is unhappy, and sees that they are very much alike after all.

In what ways do the brothers now seem similar?

Tom suggests that Ned return to the countryside and marry Cait, and although Ned admits he had been tempted the previous day, he acknowledges they made their choice a long time ago and it is now too late to go back on it. When he takes one last look at his 'picture-book' home before setting off, Ned accepts that he has outgrown it, but is still very sad to be leaving.

COMMENT

The word 'uprooted' means to be dislodged or displaced, and it is clear that by moving to Dublin, both brothers have indeed been uprooted, albeit by choice. Ned, in particular, had always wanted to live in the city, yet both brothers are still drawn back to the hillside community of their birth. In many ways, they seem out of place here: they are cultured, better educated and much more articulate than the rest of their family. However, it is here, when they escape their trapped city lives, that they feel most at home.

Compare the descriptions of the country with those of the city – which is portrayed more favourably?

A strong sense of Irish country life is created by Frank O'Connor, with vivid **descriptions** (see Literary Terms) of the people, the places and the language. Much Irish **dialect** (see Literary Terms), for example, 'breezheen' and 'aru', is used, and a local lilt is conveyed through **dialogue** (see Literary Terms) such as "Tis, 'tis, 'tis so indeed. A grand night, praise be to God' (p. 183) and 'Are ye in or are ye out, bad cess to ye!'. Occasionally, the family even talks in Irish.

At first glance, the **theme** (see Literary Terms) of love appears to be quite minor in this story. Indeed, Cait Deignan is not even mentioned until the fourth of the five sections into which the story is divided. However, it is the relationship between Ned and Cait which **symbolises** (see Literary Terms) everything about the Irish countryside from which Ned has distanced himself. Cait is a country girl, born and bred, and despite Ned's attraction to her, she **epitomises** (see Literary Terms) the life he is leaving behind. It could be said that *Uprooted* is a tale of lost love, but again, the love is lost by choice. Ned chooses to reject Cait, just as he rejects his culture in favour of a world which he still finds remote and intangible. Thus the story ends on a sad note.

GLOSSARY

guile deceit

bonhomie good will

gumption spirit, courage

skyed to hang a picture in a high position

boreen narrow unmade road

aru fool

poteen whisky illicitly distilled by Irish peasantry

ramaishing talking nonsense

A *Identify the speaker.*

1 'Of course, she used to talk of it when she was a kid, but we never paid much attention. It came as a surprise to us. I fancy it surprised the convent even more'

4 'If we were contented in ourselves the other things wouldn't matter. I suppose we must only leave it to time. Time settles everything'

2 'I presume the guards are aware that there is no test known to science that will prove the existence of lemonade in the system'

3 'But if you get it as easy as that, how do you know if it's the real thing or not?'

Identify the person 'to whom' this comment refers.

5 In that moment of revelation he had seen that the wretched occupants of the court were distracted with boredom, and he knew that the only cure for boredom was to buy something

6 He saw it as in a picture-book with all its colours intolerably bright; something he had outgrown and could never return to

8 In spite of the Sheehans' warnings she had taken him at face value, not believing him to be that sort at all

7 She was the sort of passionate girl who could very easily be lured into an indiscretion and who would then react from it in loathing and self disgust

Check your answers on page 84.

B *Consider these issues.*

a How different types of love are depicted in these stories.

b The importance of the story titles.

c How some characters seem completely unable to show or express their love.

d That love is often portrayed as being tinged with sadness or disappointment.

e How important it is that these stories are set in an Irish community.

First confession

Jackie is a seven-year-old boy who lives with his parents, his sister, Nora, and his grandmother, who came to live with the family on the death of her husband. Jackie believes this was when all his trouble began: his grandmother is rather eccentric, and Jackie is embarrassed by her behaviour. When his sister tries to make him eat a meal his grandmother has cooked, Jackie hides under the table and even lashes out at Nora with the bread-knife. After this incident, no-one in the family speaks to each other for days.

Consider how the old woman 'prepares' the pupils for their first confession – is she correct?

Jackie is about to make his first confession and communion. An old lady comes to his school to prepare the pupils, and frightens them with stories about hell. He learns what happens to people who make a 'bad confession', that is, don't tell the whole truth, and this story makes a deep impression on him. Worst of all is being taught how to examine his conscience: Jackie believes he has broken the whole ten commandments, all because of his grandmother.

On the day of his first confession, Jackie is accompanied by Nora. She torments him constantly, at first feigning sympathy for the dreadful fate which will befall him when the priest learns of the magnitude of his sins, and later, openly taunting him. Jackie is convinced his sins are too bad to tell, but he fears the consequences of making a bad confession.

Nora goes first, displaying an exaggerated exhibition of devotion, and then it is Jackie's turn. Not being used to the confessional box, he mistakes the arm rests for a place to kneel, and climbs up. He does find the position rather strange, but believes it isn't his place to criticise. When the priest becomes angry, Jackie loses his grip and tumbles out of the confessional altogether.

Why do you think the priest's attitude towards Jackie changes?

Nora, waiting outside for her brother, is embarrassed and clips him across the ear. The priest consequently defends Jackie, and realising this is his first confession, takes pity on him, and even humours him. Jackie is sent to the end of the queue on the assumption that the crimes of a lifetime will take longer to listen to than those people who are regular attenders. Jackie is impressed with the priest's logic and intelligence.

When Jackie's turn comes, the priest listens to his tales of wanting to kill his grandmother, indulging him by asking what he intends to do with her body. Jackie also confesses about the incident with Nora and the bread-knife, but by now, the priest has become quite witty, claiming he has been tempted into similar action himself on occasions, but that hanging is an awful death. By the time Jackie has finished, he is genuinely sorry to leave.

Nora is jealous when she learns that her brother has been given a small penance as a result of his first confession, and even more so when she discovers the priest has also given him a sweet. She decides being good does not pay.

COMMENT   The relationships in *First Confession* are interesting. The family obviously finds it quite difficult when

Consider the reasons why Jackie resents his grandmother so much.

another generation joins them, and Jackie in particular resents his grandmother's presence. She is on old woman, set in her ways and used to country life: he is mortified to find her drinking porter and eating with her fingers instead of a fork. Nora has obviously found a way to adapt to the situation – she 'sucked up' to her grandmother and receives a penny every Friday – but Jackie is younger and finds it harder to adjust.

In some respects, the relationship between Jackie and Nora is typical of many siblings. They bicker, they fight and they tell tales on one another. Nora uses the fact she is older to her advantage, teasing Jackie over things he has yet to experience, and exploiting his naivety and innocence. In a childish way, she enjoys making him suffer and assumes, maybe because of her own attitude to and experience of religion, that the priest will support her actions in an 'official' capacity. She hurls Jackie through the church door triumphantly, obviously relishing the thought of her brother's impending torture.

However, the priest recognises both Jackie's apprehensions regarding his first confession and his feelings of injustice regarding his grandmother. He also responds to his sincerity: Jackie is too honest to flatter his grandmother just to get a penny on Fridays, and fears the consequences too much to omit any details of his awful misdeeds. The priest humours Jackie, treating him kindly without patronising him, and teaches him some valuable lessons at the same time as easing his fears. By doing so, he shows religion in a much more favourable light than some of the other characters in the story.

GLOSSARY

fastidious particular, fussy

half-crown about 12/13 pence

penitential psalms specific psalms in the authorised Bible, said to show repentance

caffler nuisance
biretta a square cap worn by priests
retorting responding

FIRST LOVE

What is it about Mick that Peter so admires?

Peter is a sixteen-year-old office boy, described as moody, boastful and generally unsettled. As soon as he meets Mick Dowling, an eighteen-year-old university student and a very different type of person, he admires him so much that he wants to *be* him. Peter starts to imitate Mick's manners, but the people in his office ridicule him, so instead, he starts to hang around with Mick and his group of friends. At first, Mick is not interested in the friendship, and when Peter tries to impress by being profound, Mick is just puzzled. When Peter discusses religion, a topic he knows to be of interest to Mick, he only succeeds in making him antagonistic. Eventually, however, Mick and his friends accept Peter into their group, albeit as a sort of mascot.

Mick comes from a very religious family, and he confesses to Peter that he lives in dread of losing his faith. He says he is a man of uncontrollable passions and suffers agonies of conscience with Babiche Regan, his girlfriend. Peter's response is to admire Mick even more for his self-control, feel inadequate by comparison, and ruin the evening spent with Mick, Babiche and her sister Rosemary through sheer panic.

Consider how well you think Mick and Babiche are suited.

Peter does not like Babiche: he feels she is not good enough for Mick and admits he is jealous. However, when Mick leaves for university, he is so lonely that he turns to her. He sees Mick's friends but now finds them only mediocre company, and visits Mick's family, who seem to be unaware how remarkable their son is: Babiche is the only person who will happily talk about Mick the whole time.

The two spend much time together, and through imitating Mick, the person he still wants to become, Peter grows in confidence and finds himself a social success. He and Babiche have a very complex relationship: when she grows to like him, part of him enjoys it yet part of him thinks it makes her even more unworthy of Mick. On the day when they first kiss, Peter wants both to love and condemn her.

That night Peter is racked with guilt. He realises he has achieved his aim: he has become Mick and won the affections of Mick's girlfriend. However, he knows he needs Mick more than Babiche, but with horror, recognises that by proving Babiche unworthy of Mick, he has only succeeded in proving himself unworthy, too.

Peter refuses to see Babiche again, despite her encouragement, but it is too late: Mick does not call to see him when next home from university, having obviously discovered his friend's betrayal. Although, at times, Peter recognises this whole episode as part of the 'growing-pains' of becoming a man, he still has to live with the guilt of what he has done and what he has lost.

COMMENT   *First Love* explores many different types of love. The title may initially suggest love in the romantic way, but love in the sense of loyalty and commitment is also explored. It is useful to consider exactly who is the person experiencing this love, and for whom.

To Peter, Mick is a role model. They are very different in character, and the two year age gap only serves to exemplify the difference between adolescence and adulthood. Their first meeting puts Peter into a 'perfect fever' because he knows at once that Mick is the one man in the world he wants to be. Peter's feelings are those of envy, hero-worship and idolisation.

In many respects, this relationship is the 'first love' of the title.

However, Babiche is also Peter's 'first love'. Despite his misgivings about her unworthiness for Mick, Peter finds himself attracted to her. He pursues her, partly to prove how undeserving she is and partly because she genuinely seems to enjoy his company. He puts himself through agonies of self-torture, criticising Mick so she will dislike him, yet disapproving of her when she does. Every positive feeling seems to result in an accompanying negative one. During their final kiss goodnight, Peter experiences very mixed emotions.

The issue here is not just love for a girl but loyalty for a friend. Because of his relationship with Babiche, Peter feels he has 'become ten years older, full of power, peace, and self-confidence' (p. 67). However, this is outweighed by a greater kind of love, and he stops the association with Babiche going any further because of his duty to Mick, realising it was madness to have endangered his friendship with Mick over such a woman. By the time Peter acknowledges this, though, the damage has been done, and he is forced to learn a painful lesson by losing both the relationships he so valued.

GLOSSARY

bourgeois conventional

shilling five pence

ungovernable uncontrollable

apposite appropriate

synchronize coincide

armistice truce, cease-fire

prophesying predicting

nonchalance indifference

equanimity calmness

rattle-pated empty, giddy

PITY

Denis Halligan attends a boarding school deep in the country. It is not a 'good' school, and all the boys smoke, gamble and drink whenever they get a chance, but his parents are separated and it is the best his mother can afford.

One day, Denis is befriended by a new boy, Francis Cummins, who comes from his home town of Dunmore. Although Cummins is nothing like the other boys, in that he is a 'cissy' whose parents intend him to enter the priesthood, he is tolerated by them, mainly because of the food parcels sent every week from home. Denis is puzzled that Cummins's parents choose to send him away to such a school when they obviously care for him, and he becomes determined to investigate the mystery.

Compare how Mrs Cummins's views about the school differ from how it is really.

The opportunity arises during the school holidays when Denis goes to tea with the Cummins family. He discovers Mrs Cummins thinks highly of the school, and she sends her son there thinking to give him all the advantages in life that she and her husband never had. Denis cannot believe Cummins is so easily fooled, and decides he attends so willingly because of his vocation and because he thinks it is his duty.

Denis makes a point of telling his mother about Cummins's food parcels in the hope of encouraging her to be more generous, and soon after he returns to school, he receives a similar parcel. He knows his mother cannot really afford it, but his initial feelings of shame soon turn to pride in front of the other boys.

A month later, one of the boys notices the handwriting on Denis's parcels is the same as that on Cummins's parcels. Denis rereads his mother's letters, where there is no mention of the food parcels, and is forced to admit that Cummins's parents have been sending them to him.

Instead of feeling gratitude, Denis is humiliated. The parcels had represented his mother's love, which he now feels he has lost. In addition, he had thought Cummins deserved to be pitied because of his simple, shopkeeper parents, whereas all the time, they had been pitying him because he had no-one to care for him as they do their son.

Do you think Cummins deserves to be treated this way?

When he confronts Cummins and returns what is left of the parcel, Denis is in tears because he can see that Cummins's parents are right. He feels vulnerable, as if Cummins has discovered a weakness in him, and from then on, the friendship is over.

COMMENT

Consider why Cummins chooses to befriend Denis.

Both Denis and Cummins are very different characters, and it may seem unlikely that they develop such a close friendship. However, the fact that Cummins comes from the same home town appeals to Denis's sense of comradeship and appeases his secret feelings of homesick and loneliness. Although they have very little in common, their personalities seem to compliment each other.

The choice of the title *Pity* is an interesting one. Denis pities Cummins because he is different. He sees him as weak and priggish with poor, ignorant country shopkeepers for parents. He does not realise until the end of the story that all the time, these same people have been pitying him. He is a child whose parents are separated, a wild boy who is troublesome with an unsettled family background. He pictures them discussing him, the way he and his mocking mother had so patronisingly discussed Cummins.

To accept the truth of the situation leaves Denis exposed. It makes him emotional and aggressive, wanting to fight the other boys who cannot understand

his reaction and look at him curiously. Beneath the
facade of toughness Denis presents to the world is a
frightened, lonely boy who feels abandoned and
unloved. His relationship with Cummins has left this
'secret' uncovered – to continue the friendship would be
'like living naked' – and this is something that he can
never forgive.

GLOSSARY   **venial** pardonable
           altruism generosity
           conciliated bribed
           insubordination rebelliousness

THE PARAGON

The first section of this story tells how Jimmy Garvin
lives with his separated mother, a woman who ekes out
the small allowance from his father by doing housework
for rich people. Jimmy is a perfect son: intelligent and
polite, but also rather spoilt and protected.

*In what sense is
Jimmy a paragon?*

In the second section, Jimmy is about to enter
university. He is a minor celebrity, having achieved the
highest mark in Ireland in his exams, and when his
father's family sees his picture in the newspaper, they
wish to share in his glory and contact him. Jimmy's
mother is fearful of this, but Jimmy is just curious.
When his Aunt Mary suggests he visit his father in
England, Mrs Garvin becomes alarmed, but finally
relents, partly because travel will broaden Jimmy's
knowledge and partly because she wishes to show off
the son she has raised.

*Compare the
descriptions of
England with
Ireland. Which is
presented more
favourably?*

Mr Garvin meets Jimmy in London, but drives him out
into the countryside to meet the young woman he now
lives with, Martha, and Jimmy's new sister, Gussie.
This is an unexpected turn of events for Jimmy who,
full of self-righteousness, decides to ask his father

outright if he is married to Martha and to leave if not. His father is such 'a man of enthusiasms', however, that Jimmy never really has the chance to ask him directly, and when he tries, the response he gets about being in a 'thundering big mess' leaves him even more confused.

Jimmy sees many sides to his father: an outgoing, charming person who is swaggering and insolent but also someone who is kind and, at times, almost innocent, and he is obviously a popular man. He takes Jimmy to a pub, a new experience, and Jimmy likes his father and is in awe of him. Mr Garvin says he is doing fairly well financially and offers to pay Jimmy an allowance.

When Jimmy returns to Ireland, he is a changed person. He starts to frequent public houses, makes a new set of friends, finds himself a girlfriend, Anne Reidy, and begins to enjoy life. His mother is very bitter and blames this change on his father. She starts to complain to Jimmy about her marriage, but only serves to alienate her son. She thinks Jimmy will lose his scholarship if he is not careful, although Jimmy is not worried as he believes his father has money.

News then arrives to say that Mr Garvin has been arrested for embezzlement. Jimmy feels sorry for his father, despite losing his income and having to take a menial job when his scholarship fails to be renewed. He writes affectionately to him in prison, which his mother finds hard to forgive, and they have many arguments. One night, he loses his temper completely, frightening both his mother and himself, and he eventually moves out of the house. They part on good terms, though, and he visits at weekends.

Jimmy marries Anne and although he has a job at the court-house, he is studying a correspondence course for a degree, and they are very poor. They have dreadful rows but seem to enjoy them, and in their own way, are quite happy. The story ends with Jimmy and Anne, now pregnant, celebrating him achieving the degree.

What attributes, both positive and negative, has Jimmy acquired from his father?

Jimmy has turned out all right: although discovering his father brought him troubles, it also brought him the strength to handle them. He seems to have inherited the best from both parents, with the end result being 'a very fine thing'.

COMMENT

The **narrator** (see Literary Terms) of this story is an adult Larry Delaney, who is Jimmy's friend. We meet Larry's mother once more when Mrs Garvin needs support from her neighbours, and learn than she and Mick Delaney have now been together twenty-five years.

Jimmy has a close and almost exclusive relationship with his mother when he is a child. He rarely mixes with other children, and spends his time in the rich houses while his mother works, dreaming of a better life. He intends to earn money when he is older so that they can holiday abroad and have a maid. Mrs Garvin has raised him to be a 'paragon', and the expectations she places on him are tremendous: he is a child 'on whom Life has laid too heavy a burden' (p. 151).

Meeting his father and developing a relationship with him causes Jimmy to recognise his other characteristics. Mr Garvin is distinguished-looking but has a sense of quiet fun. He is very different from Jimmy's mother, who is nervous and excitable. Jimmy learns from his father how to enjoy life, be light-hearted and vibrant, and he becomes more animated and spirited.

It takes Jimmy a little while to come to terms with these new aspects of his character. Whereas before he had been so serious and careful, he now goes to the other extreme and enjoys himself rather too much. However, Jimmy is no fool and he eventually manages a compromise which results in a balanced personality. It is because of the relationships with his mother *and* his father that he develops into such a rounded personality by the end of the story.

GLOSSARY

paragon perfect example
prestige status
urbanely with sophistication
pennants banners
censorious condemning

SONG WITHOUT WORDS

Consider the importance of setting the story in a monastery.

Brother Arnold and Brother Michael live in a monastery where there is a rule of silence, although many of the monks get round this by using sign language. Brother Arnold, a jolly man with twinkling eyes, is not too keen on Brother Michael, a dull sort of man who keeps to himself.

One day, whilst trying to borrow a bottle of castor oil, Brother Arnold catches Brother Michael in a stable up to some 'shady business'. Not wishing to be involved, he leaves, but the next day Brother Michael explains, through sign language and gestures, that he had been reading the *Irish Racing News*: Brother Michael was a jockey before he entered the church. The thought of Brother Michael having such a secret makes Brother Arnold feel warm and mellow, and he immediately feels less lonely. Brother Michael lends him some newspapers, which he devours hungrily, and the two men become friends.

Brother Arnold also has a secret – a farmer whose cow he cured leaves him a bottle of beer every week behind a loose stone in the wall – and he, too, shares this, which seals the friendship. Each knows the full extent of the other's weaknesses and likes him the more for it.

They even work out a system of picking horses in races, and the loser has to pay in the form of Hail Marys. Until this point, their actions are seen by them as innocent fun.

One day, Brother Arnold acquires a pack of cards, and although Brother Michael feels this is one thing leading to another, he joins in. He is dealt an excellent hand, and wonders if the Devil is trying to tempt him. He is very apprehensive about breaking the rules of the monastery to such an extent, but Brother Arnold seems to be perfectly happy.

Think about the rules and expected behaviour of the monastery, and why the two monks behave as they do.

However, Brother Arnold's conscience finally gets the better of him: he wants to continue with the innocent amusement but knows it is wrong, and a mental struggle takes place within him. When Brother Michael gestures towards the bottle, the racing paper and the cards, Brother Arnold understands what he means, and the story ends with the two men leaving to confess to the Prior.

COMMENT   The unusual setting in the form of a silent monastery determines the style in which this story is written. The main characters do not speak, so we learn about them by the detailed **descriptions** (see Literary Terms) given of them, rather than by their words. For example, when Brother Arnold is happy to have shared a secret with Brother Michael, we are told about his 'blue eyes dancing' and his 'mischievous twinkle', and this conveys his positive feelings to the friendship. Similarly, the characters communicate with each other through gesture because no dialogue can be used, and precise phrases such as he 'bowed his head and beat his breast by way of asking pardon' are common.

The life the two monks lead is a lonely one, and the relationship they develop, even though it involves rather unusual behaviour for men of the church, brings pleasure to both of them. Brother Michael, usually a solitary figure, gains from the friendship, and after Brother Arnold sees the racing papers, he feels 'as though his heart had expanded to embrace all humanity' (p. 172).

However, with the gains come the losses. Both men are experiencing tastes of the outside world again, and growing to like them. Brother Michael tries to justify his actions to himself – he has given up his chance of a wife and children, his home and his family, his friends and his job, and only keeps something back to remind him of this – but he knows he is making excuses. His small secret represents 'the whole world' and even though it *is* a secret, he cannot hide it from God. Although some may question the actions of two religious men, it is their strength of faith which makes them confess at the end and continue with the life they have chosen, free from the temptations of the outside world.

GLOSSARY   **Adversary** The Devil
                  Prior head of a monastery

T<small>HE CHEAPJACK</small>

Why does Sam not tell Nancy how he feels about her?

Sam Higgins, a headmaster, is an educated and dignified man who lives with his sister, Delia. He finds out from Nancy MacCann, a recently widowed colleague who he regards as the pleasantest woman he has ever met, that there is to be a new teacher at the school. This worries Sam as the newcomer, Carmody, comes from Derry, as does Father Ring, a man he hates because he extracts money for the church from dying parishioners. Sam's fears are confirmed when it turns out Carmody does indeed know Father Ring.

Carmody is pompous and conceited, and Sam takes pleasure in conspiring with Nancy to mock him. When Carmody, who is from the city, rather patronisingly asks what town people do to amuse themselves, Sam points out the abbey tower and facetiously proclaims: 'When we get tired of life we chuck ourselves off that' (p. 218). He believes that Carmody may have the effect of being a 'bombshell' on the town.

Why do you think Nancy is attracted to Carmody?

Sam's dislike of Carmody is intensified when he learns he has started going out with Nancy. When Nancy calls round to see Sam and Delia, they are hurt she has not told them of her new relationship and are both very cold towards her, thereby ending their friendship. The incident puts Sam in a terrible mood, and he confides to Delia that it is all down to Carmody, whom he now suspects of turning the pupils against him.

Nancy continues to go out with Carmody and Sam continues to be jealous. At school they spend their time arguing over trivial things, and Sam finds his work is affected: school becomes torturous for him.

One day, Sam finds a diary in the playground and it turns out to belong to Carmody. Sam knows he is behaving incorrectly but he keeps the diary and reads it. He is incensed to discover Carmody's exploits with

Nancy, and to read that Carmody only wanted to see how far she would go. He also loses respect for Nancy because of her behaviour, and he now hates them equally.

Sam is about to take a dictation lesson, and without a moment's thought, begins to dictate Carmody's diary, calling it 'The Diary of a Cheapjack'. He knows he is behaving scandalously but it gives him an enormous sense of release, as though he is wreaking revenge for all the weeks of misery and humiliation he has experienced. Carmody hears the commotion made by the class, and when he discovers what Sam is doing, hits him, causing the two teachers to fight in front of the pupils. They are only brought to their senses by Nancy entering the room.

Consider why Sam chooses to leave the school.

At the end of the story, Sam picks up his things and leaves the school for the last time. The following day he goes away from the area completely and never returns.

COMMENT   Jealousy can make people behave in ways which are totally out of character. From the very beginning, we learn that Sam Higgins is a respectable, decent, professional man, a man who suffers from nerves and dyspepsia, and who behaves in what he considers a 'proper' manner by not declaring his feelings to Nancy because she is barely out of mourning for her first husband. This is hardly the sort of character we expect to be involved in a brawl.

However, Sam's relationship with Carmody changes him completely. He dislikes the man even before he arrives because of his connection with Father Ring (incidentally, the same Father Ring as in *The Miser*), and his nick-naming him the Bombshell is rather prophetic: Carmody does indeed cause an explosion in the town and especially in the life of Sam Higgins. The fact that Carmody giggles while he proudly admits to being a Bombshell, and does so whilst glancing at Nancy, may even suggest that his actions are intentional.

Carmody is not an honourable man. He admits in his diary he first made love to Nancy just for the practice, and even writes of the moment he stopped despising her. Sam *is* an honourable man. He is completely jealous, and incensed that a fellow teacher could behave this way. By using the diary in the way he does, and by openly fighting in front of his pupils, he has been reduced to the same level as Carmody. It is because he is 'As decent a man as ever drew breath but too honest, too honest!' (p. 227) that he has to leave.

GLOSSARY   **cheapjack** a travelling salesman who claims to sell wonderful bargains that are really worthless

dyspepsia indigestion

pseudo- pretend

Byronic from Byron, a romantic poet

A *Identify the speaker.*

1 He had to put his head on one side to see me, and I had to put mine on one side to see him, so we were more or less talking to one another upside-down

4 'I made a bit of a fool of myself but Father had nothing to do with that'

2 'I suppose we all have our little hiding-hole if the truth was known, but as small as it is, the whole world is in it, and bit by bit it grows on us again till the day You find us out'

3 'If anyone told me that thing was written by an educated man I'd call him a liar'

Identify the person 'to whom' this comment refers.

5 He had the sort of face you would expect to see advertising somebody's tobacco: a big, innocent, contented face with a pair of blue eyes that were always twinkling

6 His mistake had been in trying to become Mick in the outside world as well, for in that process he had become something which the real Mick would despise

8 Now, whatever he had inherited from his parents, he had combined it into something that belonged to neither of them, that was his only, and a very fine thing it seemed to me

7 He cried because he had thought he was keeping his secret so well and that no one but himself knew how little toughness and insubordination there was in him till Cummins had come and pried it out

Check your answers on page 84.

B *Consider these issues.*

a How relationships develop and change because of specific events.

B The importance of the story titles.

C How the way characters are initially described affects our opinion of them.

D The way religion is portrayed in these stories.

E How important it is that these stories are set in an Irish community.

PART THREE

COMMENTARY

THEMES, LANGUAGE AND STYLE

Look at other ways of categorising and grouping these stories.

The stories have been categorised into four thematic sections: Childhood, the Irish Community, Love and Relationships. Although there are other possible ways of grouping the texts, and there is also considerable overlap, these subsections serve as interesting starting points for discussion.

Childhood

Childhood is a common and significant theme in Frank O'Connor's short stories. 'Childhood' here incorporates *My Oedipus Complex*, *The Genius*, *The Study of History* and *The Duke's Children*, all texts which focus on the developing Larry Delaney. The stories, often **anecdotal** (see Literary Terms) in nature, concern the misunderstandings that arise through innocence and inexperience, and Larry's naivety is conveyed in a simple style, usually with a tone of pleasant intimacy and an element of whimsical humour.

The Irish Community

'The Irish Community' consists of *The Bridal Night*, *In the Train*, *The Miser* and *The Majesty of the Law*. These stories include several descriptive passages of character or setting, and often a distinct **atmosphere** (see Literary Terms) is created. Whether presented in a favourable or unfavourable light, the importance of belonging to a close-knit Irish community, and the effect it has on people's beliefs and behaviour, is emphasised throughout.

Love

Many of Frank O'Connor's stories focus on the theme of love. 'Love' here contains *The Ugly Duckling*, *Don Juan's Temptation*, *A Salesman's Romance* and *Uprooted*, although it could just as easily have included several of the other texts. These stories deal with rather unconventional types of love: enduring and warm;

superficial and sexual; short-lived and shallow; and unfulfilled. They are often sad and even nostalgic in **tone** (see Literary Terms).

Relationships   'Relationships', again, could have included many of Frank O'Connor's stories, but concentrates here on *First Confession, First Love, Pity, The Paragon, Song Without Words* and *The Cheapjack*. The relationships cover family, friendship and romantic liaisons, and this is probably the most diverse of the thematic categories in terms of written style, ranging from total narrative and description in *Song Without Words* to the plentiful dialogue of *The Cheapjack*, from humour to sadness and from complex to straightforward.

STRUCTURE

There are specific features which identify a short story as a genre separate from other forms of prose fiction, and the structure is often very distinct.

LENGTH

One obvious and significant feature where a story differs from a novel is the length. Many writers adopt the genre of the short story because it allows them to explore ideas and issues within a format which is more manageable and self-contained. A novel tends to demand a great deal of detail, with descriptions of place, setting and character vital to the maintenance of the storyline. The writer of the short story does not have the opportunity to elaborate upon such features, although in the case of Frank O'Connor, place, setting and character do tend to be developed quite fully within a short story framework.

Short stories rarely contain the subplots which are to be found in novels, and often the main focus is simply a character or an event. *Song Without Words*, for example, concentrates almost entirely on the characters of Brother Arnold and Brother Michael, and *Don Juan's Temptation* concerns one specific incident, the meeting of Gussie Leonard and Helen, as does *The Bridal Night*, with the focus being the night spent together by Denis Sullivan and Winnie Regan, told through the devise of a flashback.

Texts like these, by their very nature, have a very short time-span, whereas other stories in the collection cover a much longer period of time. *The Ugly Duckling* starts when Nan is a teenager and ends many years later, when she is a nun living in a convent. Although a short story is complete in its own right and there is no need for chapter breaks, *The Ugly Duckling*, as well as some of the other longer stories such as *The Genius*, *In the Train*, *The Paragon*, *Uprooted*, *The Miser* and *The Cheapjack*, is divided into subsections, almost mini-chapters, so that Frank O'Connor can show the progression through time and sometimes place.

BEGINNINGS AND ENDINGS

A novel will often begin with a lengthy, detailed introduction, taking time to familiarise the reader with the events and circumstances concerned, but a short story does not have that luxury: it has to attract a reader's attention immediately. Because of this, many short stories have opening sentences which create a very strong impact.

The first line of *The Study of History* reads: 'The discovery of where babies came from filled my life with excitement and interest'. Such an introduction is designed to engage a reader, as are the opening lines of *Song Without Words*, *Don Juan's Temptation* and *The Genius*. Frank O'Connor also uses story openings to create a sense of place, as in *The Bridal Night*, and to capture a character, as in *Uprooted* and *The Miser*. One text, *In The Train*, starts with dialogue (see Literary Terms) mid-conversation, which serves to add to the mystery and uncertainty which pervade the whole story.

Because of the need to create a sense of completeness about the short story, it is customary for them to have strong endings which give a definite sense of **closure** (see Literary Terms). Some stories in this collection, such as *The Paragon*, end very positively, whilst others, namely *Pity* and *First Love*, conclude on a very sad note. One text, *The Miser*, actually ends with a 'twist in the tail', but usually, rather than being very dramatic, Frank O'Connor's favourite devise is to end in a very simple way, for example, the last line of *The Miser* – 'Then he took his shabby old soft hat and went home'.

CHARACTERS

Often with short stories, there is neither the time nor the space, as there is with the novel, to develop characters into fully rounded individuals. However, one of Frank O'Connor's strengths as a writer is that by the end of a short story, we often feel we know a character very well. Because he focuses on human nature, we can easily relate to the people in his stories: their feelings, their beliefs, their way of behaving and of responding to others. This is especially true when a character, such as Larry Delaney, appears in several stories.

PART FOUR

STUDY SKILLS

HOW TO USE QUOTATIONS

One of the secrets of success in writing essays is the way you use quotations. There are five basic principles:
- Put inverted commas at the beginning and end of the quotation
- Write the quotation exactly as it appears in the original
- Do not use a quotation that repeats what you have just written
- Use the quotation so that it fits into your sentence
- Keep the quotation as short as possible

Quotations should be used to develop the line of thought in your essays.

Your comment should not duplicate what is in your quotation. For example:

> Frank O'Connor ends the story by describing how Larry's father went out of his way to buy him a model railway: 'At Christmas he went out of his way to buy me a really nice model railway'.

Far more effective is to write:

> Frank O'Connor ends the story by describing how Larry's father tried especially hard to cement their relationship: 'At Christmas he went out of his way to buy me a really nice model railway'.

However, the most sophisticated way of using the writer's words is to embed them into your sentence:

> In order to emphasise the cementing of the relationship, Frank O'Connor ends the story on a positive note with Larry's father going 'out of his way' to treat him to 'a really nice model railway' for Christmas.

When you use quotations in this way, you are demonstrating the ability to use text as evidence to support your ideas - not simply including words from the original to prove you have read it.

Everyone writes differently. Work through the suggestions given here and adapt the advice to suit your own style and interests. This will improve your essay-writing skills and allow your personal voice to emerge.

The following points indicate in ascending order the skills of essay writing:

- Picking out one or two facts about the story and adding the odd detail
- Writing about the text by retelling the story
- Retelling the story and adding a quotation here and there
- Organising an answer which explains what is happening in the text and giving quotations to support what you write

....

- Writing in such a way as to show that you have thought about the intentions of the writer of the text and that you understand the techniques used
- Writing at some length, giving your viewpoint on the text and commenting by picking out details to support your views
- Looking at the text as a work of art, demonstrating clear critical judgement and explaining to the reader of your essay how the enjoyment of the text is assisted by literary devices, linguistic effects and psychological insights; showing how the text relates to the time when it was written

The dotted line above represents the division between lower and higher level grades. Higher-level performance begins when you start to consider your response as a reader of the text. The highest level is reached when you offer an enthusiastic personal response and show how this piece of literature is a product of its time.

Coursework essay

Set aside an hour or so at the start of your work to plan what you have to do.

- List all the points you feel are needed to cover the task. Collect page references of information and quotations that will support what you have to say. A helpful tool is the highlighter pen: this saves painstaking copying and enables you to target precisely what you want to use.
- Focus on what you consider to be the main points of the essay. Try to sum up your argument in a single sentence, which could be the closing sentence of your essay. Depending on the essay title, it could be a statement about a character: by the end, Gussie Leonard can feel nothing but relief as he takes on the facade of a Don Juan once more.; an opinion about setting: the environment described at the end of *In The Train*, with its remote cottages and rocks at the water's edge, only serves to emphasise Helena's isolation in a community where she is not really accepted.; or a judgement on a theme: the contrast between the countryside and the city is shown finally at the end of *Uprooted*, where Ned Keating rejects his provincial home and all it represents forever.
- Make a short essay plan. Use the first paragraph to introduce the argument you wish to make. In the following paragraphs develop this argument with details, examples and other possible points of view. Sum up your argument in the last paragraph. Check you have answered the question.
- Write the essay, remembering all the time the central point you are making.
- On completion, go back over what you have written to eliminate careless errors and improve expression. Read it aloud to yourself, or, if you are feeling more confident, to a relative or friend.

If you can, try to type your essay, using a word processor. This will allow you to correct and improve your writing without spoiling its appearance.

Examination essay

The essay written in an examination often carries more marks than the coursework essay even though it is written under considerable time pressure.

In the revision period build up notes on various aspects of the text you are using. Fortunately, in acquiring this set of York Notes on *My Oedipus Complex and Other Stories*, you have made a prudent beginning! York Notes are set out to give you vital information and help you to construct your personal overview of the text.

Make notes with appropriate quotations about the key issues of the set text. Go into the examination knowing your text and having a clear set of opinions about it.

In most English Literature examinations you can take in copies of your set books. This in an enormous advantage although it may lull you into a false sense of security. Beware! There is simply not enough time in an examination to read the book from scratch.

In the examination

- Read the question paper carefully and remind yourself what you have to do.
- Look at the questions on your set texts to select the one that most interests you and mentally work out the points you wish to stress.
- Remind yourself of the time available and how you are going to use it.
- Briefly map out a short plan in note form that will keep your writing on track and illustrate the key argument you want to make.
- Then set about writing it.
- When you have finished, check through to eliminate errors.

To summarise,
these are the
keys to success:

- Know the text
- Have a clear understanding of and opinions on the storyline, characters, setting, themes and writer's concerns
- Select the right material
- Plan and write a clear response, continually bearing the question in mind

SAMPLE ESSAY PLAN

A typical essay question on *My Oedipus Complex and Other Stories* is followed by a sample essay plan in note form. This does not present the only answer to the question, merely one answer. Do not be afraid to include your own ideas and leave out some of the ones in this sample! Remember that quotations are essential to prove and illustrate the points you make.

With reference to at least two of Frank O'Connor's short stories, discuss how he conveys the innocence and naivety of childhood. Which story do you find more successful, and why?

Introduction   Rephrase the question; explain which two stories you are going to use, for example, *My Oedipus Complex* and *The Genius*, and briefly explain why these two are a good choice to discuss the innocence and naivety of childhood.

Part 1   Bearing the question in mind throughout, look in more detail at *My Oedipus Complex*. Set the character of Larry into some sort of context – aged about five, close relationship with mother, father returning from war – and discuss how his treatment of the situation is typical of a young child. You could highlight the innocence and simplicity of his life *before* his father's return, with Mrs Left and Mrs Right discussing all his problems; some of his naive ideas such as where babies come from, and praying to God to return his father to war;

and how he behaves in such a childish way as a result of his jealousy, for example, copying his father, kicking him in bed and having a screaming temper tantrum. Think about the style in which the story is written, as well as the content, and comment on the effects of Frank O'Connor's gentle humour. Remember to quote to support what you say.

Part 2   Still focusing on the question, now look in more detail at *The Genius*, cross-referencing what you say with *My Oedipus Complex* whenever relevant. Again, some sort of context is needed, and you then to consider how Larry behaves and what he says which reveals how innocent and naive he really is. You could, for example, discuss his views on where babies come from (an obvious point of cross-reference) and how they are made with starting handles and motors; his rather condescending attitude to his parents; and his reaction to what he perceives as a rejection from Una. Again, try to comment on the style as well as the content, quoting to support your points.

Part 3   Explain which of the stories you find more successful, and why. This is a personal opinion, but needs to be rooted in the texts. You could refer briefly to your own experiences to show how perceptive Frank O'Connor is about childhood.

Conclusion   Referring back to the title, draw your essay to a close by briefly summing up how successful Frank O'Connor is in conveying the innocence and naivety of childhood.

FURTHER QUESTIONS

Here are more questions on the short story. Work out what your answer would be, always being sure to draw up a plan first.

1 'The Irish community is portrayed as a powerful and influential aspect of people's lives, whether for positive or negative reasons.' Discuss this statement in the light of two or three of Frank O'Connor's short stories.

2 Frank O'Connor often writes on the theme of love. To what extent is this love tinged with sadness or disappointment? Refer to at least two stories in your answer.

3 Compare and contrast the main relationships in three of Frank O'Connor's short stories.

4 With reference to two or three stories, discuss how the church is portrayed in Ireland, and consider the importance of religion to the Irish people.

5 Look at Frank O'Connor's technique of combining humour and seriousness when creating the character of Larry Delaney. How effective do you find this technique to be?

6 There is a clear divide between the town and the country in the work of Frank O'Connor. How do they differ and which is presented more favourably? Refer to three or four stories in your answer.

7 Which of Frank O'Connor's short stories have you most enjoyed and why? Try to comment on setting, plot, character, themes and also style.

8 With reference to two or three stories, discuss Frank O'Connor's treatment of outsiders, explaining what makes these people so different from the rest of the world.

9 What do you learn about Ireland and the Irish people from the short stories of Frank O'Connor. Refer to at least two stories in your answer.

10 Frank O'Connor has been described as 'One of the masters of the short story' by V.S. Pritchett. With detailed reference to at least three of his stories, explain to what extent you agree with this statement.

PART FIVE

CULTURAL CONNECTIONS

BROADER PERSPECTIVES

Despite the words 'short' and 'story' sounding rather unimpressive, and perhaps a genre perceived as an 'easier' option both to write and study, many of our greatest writers have written at their very best in short story form: Henry James, Joseph Conrad and D.H. Lawrence to name but a few.

Frank O'Connor is one of the great writers of the modern Irish short story, and it is worth examining other Irish short story writers in order to place his work in context: Mary Lavin, Liam O'Flaherty and Sean O'Faolain are the three most notable. Mary Lavin writes about all aspects of Irish culture, often concentrating on the theme of the role of women in Irish life. This can be compared with the closely and simply focused local concern of Liam O'Flaherty and the more international stance of Sean O'Faolain. All these short story writers give further insight to the work of Frank O'Connor, and in terms of how Ireland is presented in other genre, James Joyce, the novelist, W.B. Yeats, the poet, and J.M. Synge, the playwright, are also worth considering.

For other collections of short stories on the theme of childhood, read *Dandelion Clocks*, edited by Alfred Bradley and Kay Jamieson (Penguin, 1978), a bitter-sweet anthology in which the stories capture the essence of childhood in moods of nostalgia, affection, pain and bewilderment, and *Modern Short Stories in English*, selected and introduced by Barrie Wade (Arnold-Wheaton, 1980), a collection varied in style and treatment and arranged chronologically from childhood to adolescence.

ambiguous more than one valid interpretation

analogy a parallel or likeness

anecdote a narrative of a small incident or event

atmosphere the mood which dominates a piece of writing

chronology time sequence of a list of events

closure the impression of completeness achieved at the end of a short story

context the surrounding circumstances to give a framework for understanding

description the creation in words of objects, people, behaviour or scenes

dialect language particular to a region or group of people

dialogue conversation of characters

empathy/empathise total involvement and understanding with another

epitome/epitomise absolute representation

first person narrative a story told by one of the characters, using 'I'

image a visual picture

irony a subtle kind of sarcasm where what is said is the opposite of what is meant

metaphor an implied though unstated comparison

mood atmosphere or tone

narrator the person telling the story

paradox an apparent contradiction

pathetic fallacy a technique where the weather is used to define atmosphere

symbol one thing used to represent another

theme a central idea

viewpoint perspective

TEST ANSWERS

TEST YOURSELF (Section I: Childhood)

A 1 Larry *(My Oedipus Complex)*
2 Larry *(The Duke's Children)*
3 Larry *(The Study of History)*
4 Larry *(The Genius)*
5 Una Dwyer *(The Genius)*
6 Father *(My Oedipus Complex)*
7 Father *(The Duke's Children)*
8 Mother *(My Oedipus Complex)*

TEST YOURSELF (Section II: The Irish Community)

A 1 Magner *(In The Train)*
2 Father Ring *(The Miser)*
3 Winnie Regan *(The Bridal Night)*
4 The sergeant *(The Majesty of the Law)*
5 Denis Sullivan *(The Bridal Night)*
6 The sergeant's wife *(In The Train)*
7 Dan Bride *(The Majesty of the Law)*
8 Tom Devereux *(The Miser)*

TEST YOURSELF (Section III: Love)

A 1 Dinny Ryan *(The Ugly Duckling)*
2 Charlie Ford *(A Salesman's Romance)*
3 Helen *(Don Juan's Temptation)*
4 Ned Keating *(Uprooted)*
5 Charlie Ford *(A Salesman's Romance)*
6 Ned Keating *(Uprooted)*
7 Nan Ryan *(The Ugly Duckling)*
8 Gussie Leonard *(Don Juan's Temptation)*

TEST YOURSELF (Section IV: Relationships)

A 1 Jackie *(First Confession)*
2 Brother Michael *(Song Without Words)*
3 Sam Higgins *(The Cheapjack)*
4 Jimmy Garvin *(The Paragon)*
5 Brother Arnold *(Song Without Words)*
6 Peter *(First Love)*
7 Denis Halligan *(Pity)*
8 Jimmy Garvin *(The Paragon)*

GCSE and equivalent levels (£3.50 each)

Maya Angelou
I Know Why the Caged Bird Sings

Jane Austen
Pride and Prejudice

Alan Ayckbourn
Absent Friends

Elizabeth Barrett Browning
Selected Poems

Robert Bolt
A Man for All Seasons

Harold Brighouse
Hobson's Choice

Charlotte Brontë
Jane Eyre

Emily Brontë
Wuthering Heights

Shelagh Delaney
A Taste of Honey

Charles Dickens
David Copperfield

Charles Dickens
Great Expectations

Charles Dickens
Hard Times

Charles Dickens
Oliver Twist

Roddy Doyle
Paddy Clarke Ha Ha Ha

George Eliot
Silas Marner

George Eliot
The Mill on the Floss

William Golding
Lord of the Flies

Oliver Goldsmith
She Stoops To Conquer

Willis Hall
The Long and the Short and the Tall

Thomas Hardy
Far from the Madding Crowd

Thomas Hardy
The Mayor of Casterbridge

Thomas Hardy
Tess of the d'Urbervilles

Thomas Hardy
The Withered Arm and other Wessex Tales

L.P. Hartley
The Go-Between

Seamus Heaney
Selected Poems

Susan Hill
I'm the King of the Castle

Barry Hines
A Kestrel for a Knave

Louise Lawrence
Children of the Dust

Harper Lee
To Kill a Mockingbird

Laurie Lee
Cider with Rosie

Arthur Miller
The Crucible

Arthur Miller
A View from the Bridge

Robert O'Brien
Z for Zachariah

Frank O'Connor
My Oedipus Complex and other stories

George Orwell
Animal Farm

J.B. Priestley
An Inspector Calls

Willy Russell
Educating Rita

Willy Russell
Our Day Out

J.D. Salinger
The Catcher in the Rye

William Shakespeare
Henry IV Part 1

William Shakespeare
Henry V

William Shakespeare
Julius Caesar

William Shakespeare
Macbeth

William Shakespeare
The Merchant of Venice

William Shakespeare
A Midsummer Night's Dream

William Shakespeare
Much Ado About Nothing

William Shakespeare
Romeo and Juliet

William Shakespeare
The Tempest

William Shakespeare
Twelfth Night

George Bernard Shaw
Pygmalion

Mary Shelley
Frankenstein

R.C. Sherriff
Journey's End

Rukshana Smith
Salt on the snow

John Steinbeck
Of Mice and Men

Robert Louis Stevenson
Dr Jekyll and Mr Hyde

Jonathan Swift
Gulliver's Travels

Robert Swindells
Daz 4 Zoe

Mildred D. Taylor
Roll of Thunder, Hear My Cry

Mark Twain
Huckleberry Finn

James Watson
Talking in Whispers

William Wordsworth
Selected Poems

A Choice of Poets

Mystery Stories of the Nineteenth Century including The Signalman

Nineteenth Century Short Stories

Poetry of the First World War

Six Women Poets

York Notes Advanced (£3.99 each)

Margaret Atwood
The Handmaid's Tale

Jane Austen
Mansfield Park

Jane Austen
Persuasion

Jane Austen
Pride and Prejudice

Alan Bennett
Talking Heads

William Blake
Songs of Innocence and of Experience

Charlotte Brontë
Jane Eyre

Emily Brontë
Wuthering Heights

Geoffrey Chaucer
The Franklin's Tale

Geoffrey Chaucer
General Prologue to the Canterbury Tales

Geoffrey Chaucer
The Wife of Bath's Prologue and Tale

Joseph Conrad
Heart of Darkness

Charles Dickens
Great Expectations

John Donne
Selected Poems

George Eliot

The Mill on the Floss

F. Scott Fitzgerald
The Great Gatsby

E.M. Forster
A Passage to India

Brian Friel
Translations

Thomas Hardy
The Mayor of Casterbridge

Thomas Hardy
Tess of the d'Urbervilles

Seamus Heaney
Selected Poems from Opened Ground

Nathaniel Hawthorne
The Scarlet Letter

James Joyce
Dubliners

John Keats
Selected Poems

Christopher Marlowe
Doctor Faustus

Arthur Miller
Death of a Salesman

Toni Morrison
Beloved

William Shakespeare
Antony and Cleopatra

William Shakespeare
As You Like It

William Shakespeare
Hamlet

William Shakespeare
King Lear

William Shakespeare
Measure for Measure

William Shakespeare
The Merchant of Venice

William Shakespeare
Much Ado About Nothing

William Shakespeare
Othello

William Shakespeare
Romeo and Juliet

William Shakespeare
The Tempest

William Shakespeare
The Winter's Tale

Mary Shelley
Frankenstein

Alice Walker
The Color Purple

Oscar Wilde
The Importance of Being Earnest

Tennessee Williams
A Streetcar Named Desire

John Webster
The Duchess of Malfi

W.B. Yeats
Selected Poems

Chinua Achebe
Things Fall Apart

Edward Albee
Who's Afraid of Virginia Woolf?

Margaret Atwood
Cat's Eye

Jane Austen
Emma

Jane Austen
Northanger Abbey

Jane Austen
Sense and Sensibility

Samuel Beckett
Waiting for Godot

Robert Browning
Selected Poems

Robert Burns
Selected Poems

Angela Carter
Nights at the Circus

Geoffrey Chaucer
The Merchant's Tale

Geoffrey Chaucer
The Miller's Tale

Geoffrey Chaucer
The Nun's Priest's Tale

Samuel Taylor Coleridge
Selected Poems

Daniel Defoe
Moll Flanders

Daniel Defoe
Robinson Crusoe

Charles Dickens
Bleak House

Charles Dickens
Hard Times

Emily Dickinson
Selected Poems

Carol Ann Duffy
Selected Poems

George Eliot
Middlemarch

T.S. Eliot
The Waste Land

T.S. Eliot
Selected Poems

Henry Fielding
Joseph Andrews

E.M. Forster
Howards End

John Fowles
The French Lieutenant's Woman

Robert Frost
Selected Poems

Elizabeth Gaskell
North and South

Stella Gibbons
Cold Comfort Farm

Graham Greene
Brighton Rock

Thomas Hardy
Jude the Obscure

Thomas Hardy
Selected Poems

Joseph Heller
Catch-22

Homer
The Iliad

Homer
The Odyssey

Gerard Manley Hopkins
Selected Poems

Aldous Huxley
Brave New World

Kazuo Ishiguro
The Remains of the Day

Ben Jonson
The Alchemist

Ben Jonson
Volpone

James Joyce
A Portrait of the Artist as a Young Man

Philip Larkin
Selected Poems

D.H. Lawrence
The Rainbow

D.H. Lawrence
Selected Stories

D.H. Lawrence
Sons and Lovers

D.H. Lawrence
Women in Love

John Milton
Paradise Lost Bks I & II

John Milton
Paradise Lost Bks IV & IX

Thomas More
Utopia

Sean O'Casey
Juno and the Paycock

George Orwell
Nineteen Eighty-four

John Osborne
Look Back in Anger

Wilfred Owen
Selected Poems

Sylvia Plath
Selected Poems

Alexander Pope
Rape of the Lock and other poems

Ruth Prawer Jhabvala
Heat and Dust

Jean Rhys
Wide Sargasso Sea

William Shakespeare
As You Like It

William Shakespeare
Coriolanus

William Shakespeare
Henry IV Pt 1

William Shakespeare
Henry V

William Shakespeare
Julius Caesar

William Shakespeare
Macbeth

William Shakespeare
Measure for Measure

William Shakespeare
A Midsummer Night's Dream

William Shakespeare
Richard II

FUTURE TITLES (continued)

William Shakespeare
Richard III

William Shakespeare
Sonnets

William Shakespeare
The Taming of the Shrew

William Shakespeare
Twelfth Night

William Shakespeare
The Winter's Tale

George Bernard Shaw
Arms and the Man

George Bernard Shaw
Saint Joan

Muriel Spark
The Prime of Miss Jean Brodie

John Steinbeck
The Grapes of Wrath

John Steinbeck
The Pearl

Tom Stoppard
Arcadia

Tom Stoppard
*Rosencrantz and Guildenstern
are Dead*

Jonathan Swift
*Gulliver's Travels and The
Modest Proposal*

Alfred, Lord Tennyson
Selected Poems

W.M. Thackeray
Vanity Fair

Virgil
The Aeneid

Edith Wharton
The Age of Innocence

Tennessee Williams
Cat on a Hot Tin Roof

Tennessee Williams
The Glass Menagerie

Virginia Woolf
Mrs Dalloway

Virginia Woolf
To the Lighthouse

William Wordsworth
Selected Poems

Metaphysical Poets